THE ULTIMATE **MANCHESTER UNITED** QUIZ BOOK

THE ULTIMATE **MANCHESTER UNITED** QUIZ BOOK

Reach Sport

Published in Great Britain and Ireland in 2022 by
Reach Sport, a Reach PLC business,
5 St Paul's Square, Liverpool, L3 9SJ.

Reach Sport

www.reachsport.com
@reach_sport

Reach Sport is a part of Reach PLC.
One Canada Square, Canary Wharf, London, E15 5AP.

ISBN: 9781914197208
eBook ISBN: 9781914197215

Photographic acknowledgements:
Reach PLC, Alamy, Getty Images.

With special thanks to John D.T. White

Printed and bound in Great Britain by
CPI Group (UK) Ltd, Croydon, CR0 4YY.

CONTENTS

THE ULTIMATE **MANCHESTER UNITED** QUIZ BOOK

QUESTION-SETTERS
Ben Ashby, Steve Bartram, Adam Bostock, Sam Carney, Paul Davies, Mark Froggatt, Joe Ganley, Charlie Ghagan, Matthew Holt, Ian McLeish, Adam Marshall, Sean Mullan, Mikey Partington, Harry Robinson, John White

PUBLISHED BY Reach Sport
Managing Director Steve Hanrahan, **Commercial Director** Will Beedles, **Executive Editor** Paul Dove, **Executive Art Editor** Rick Cooke, **Production Editor** Adam Oldfield, **Production Journalist** Simon Monk, **Designer** Mark Frances

EARLY YEARS

From our Newton Heath roots to the new-look Manchester United

1. In what year was the club, first known as Newton Heath LYR, believed to have been established?

1878

2. What did the 'LYR' stand for, referring to the industry from within which the club sprung? Lancashire AND YORKShire RAILWAY

3. The club's official league records begin in 1892/93, competing for the first time in the Football League. Against which Lancashire side (still well known today) did Newton Heath play their first league game, losing 4-3?

BLACK BURN ROVERS

4. What was the name of the club's first home ground?

5. The club's first-ever victory in league football came by an extraordinary scoreline, which still stands (as of April 2022) as the club's joint-biggest winning margin in league football. Wolverhampton Wanderers were the victims – how many goals did Newton Heath score in the game?

6. What was the name of the club's next home ground, moved to at the start of the 1893/94 season?

7. What was the name of the wealthy Manchester businessman who provided financial backing to help save the club from going out of business in 1902?

8. When this change of ownership came into effect, there was also a change of name from Newton Heath to Manchester United. What other significant change to the club's identity was made?

9. What was the name of the 'club secretary' (manager in modern terminology) who arrived at the club in 1903 from Burnley, and whose first major success was leading United to promotion from the Second Division in the 1905/06 season?

10. What feat (a first, and only repeated once since, in 2004) did forward Charles Sagar achieve in his first Manchester United game, having been signed from Bury, a 5-1 win over Bristol City in September 1905?

11. A famous first league title came in 1907/08. Which Midlands club were runners-up to Manchester United in the table that season?

12. In 1910, the club moved to a third stadium in as many decades, but this time for the long-term: Old Trafford. Who was the name of the famous stadium architect who designed the ground?

13. The first official game at Old Trafford, in February 1910, ended in defeat – to which rival?

14. On top of that maiden league title, and then FA Cup victory in 1909, in which season did a second league title arrive – a third major trophy triumph to underline a glorious era?

15. Harold Halse achieved what goalscoring feat in the 8-4 Charity Shield win over Swindon Town in September 1911 – a first in club history, and only once repeated since?

Identify the following five playing stars of the early era...

16. Scottish striker signed in 1893, then re-signed in 1895; first player ever to reach a century of goals for the club; played 174 times and scored 100 goals between 1893 and 1900.

17. Signed from Grimsby in 1904, this Darlington-born player became United captain and, alongside Dick Duckworth and Alex Bell, formed a famed half-back trio; played 302 games for the club between 1904 and 1913.

18. An exciting left-winger hailing from Sunderland, he signed from Barnsley in 1906 and went on to play 319 games for United (a record at the time) and score 100 goals (third player in club history to reach a century) between 1906 and 1915.

19. Legendary toothpick-chewing Welsh winger, signed from Manchester City in 1906, who went on to play well into his 40s for United, making 335 appearances in total – a new club appearance record at the time, set in 1921.

20. Scottish striker also signed from Man City in 1906, who was excellent in the air. Played 247 games between 1906 and 1915, and was the second player to reach 100 United goals, finishing with 101 in total (among them a famous trophy-winner).

21. Who was the young striker – born in Throckley, Northumberland – who made his United debut in August 1919 and would go on to smash both the club's appearances record (510 games) and goalscoring record (168 goals) in a legendary career lasting until 1933?

22. Who did United sign from Aston Villa in 1922, an all-action player with a reputation as a hardman (and with a record of scrapes with the game's authorities), who skippered the Reds and made 152 appearances between 1922 and 1928?

23. What was unusual about the managerial spell of Clarence 'Lal' Hilditch between October 1926 and April 1927? *(Clue: It wouldn't happen again at the club until 2014).*

24. What foodstuff apparently sweetened the deal that took young amateur Hugh McLenahan to Old Trafford from Stockport County in 1927, courtesy of United scout and fixer Louis Rocca?

25. During a difficult period for the club, United succumbed to a record defeat by the same scoreline three times, in 1926 (Blackburn Rovers), in 1930 (Aston Villa) and in 1931 (Wolverhampton Wanderers). What was that scoreline?

26. The club faced financial trouble once more in the early 1930s. Who was the local businessman who became involved in the club and invested vital money in 1931, to 'save' Manchester United a second time?

27. A promising youngster emerged into the United team in the 1936/37 season, but would find much greater recognition later as England manager from 1946 to 1962, eventually being knighted for services to sport in 1978. Who?

28. Who was the young Irishman who made a first-team debut in September 1937, who would later go on to captain the club with distinction and compile 344 appearances?

29. A future club-record goalscorer notched his first United goals – four of them! – in only his second senior appearance in December 1937, against Swansea. Who?

30. What did the initials 'MUJAC' stand for, the basis of the club's famous youth system established in 1938?

1946-1959

A period of triumph and tragedy overseen by a visionary Scot

1. The Manchester United manager's role, taken up in 1945, was Matt Busby's third in management, having already managed Manchester City and Liverpool – true or false?

2. On the resumption of league football after World War II, at which ground did United play their home fixture against Grimsby Town to begin the 1946/47 campaign?

3. Identify the missing player in that first post-War league line-up selected by Busby, one of the scorers (the other was Charlie Mitten) in a 2-1 win: Jack Crompton, Johnny Carey, Billy McGlen, Jack Warner, Allenby Chilton, Henry Cockburn, Jimmy Delaney, Stan Pearson, Jimmy Hanlon, Charlie Mitten, ---- ------.

4. One of the above line-up was Matt Busby's first transfer outlay, bought for £4,000 from Celtic (Ted Buckle having been Busby's first signing, but for free). Who?

5. Four games into that 1946/47 season, United thrashed Liverpool 5-0. Who scored a hat-trick that day, a Salford-born inside forward who'd score a famous FA Cup semi-final hat-trick the following season and end up with a total of 148 goals from 343 matches?

6. Two games later, in a 1-1 draw with Chelsea, a player who would go on to make 284 appearances over the next eight seasons made his debut – and someone whose son would appear for United in the 1968 European Cup final. Who?

7. Jack Rowley scored 26 league goals during 1946/47, setting a new club record for number of league goals scored in a season – whose record did he break, a famous Scottish striker who had set the mark during the 1907/08 title-winning campaign?

8. What did the 1946/47 season have in common with the 1947/48, 1948/49 and 1950/51 season in terms of the final table?

9. Why did United play two 'home' games in the FA Cup campaign of 1948 at Everton's ground Goodison Park and Huddersfield Town's Leeds Road stadium?

10. Who was the talented inside-forward who, after a falling-out with manager Busby, was sold to Derby County for a record fee in March 1949, replaced by John Downie bought from Bradford Park Avenue?

11. What was significant about the location of the first home game of the 1949/50 season, in which United beat Bolton 3-0?

12. What feat of goalscoring did Charlie Mitten achieve, in the process of scoring four goals in a 7-0 thrashing of Aston Villa in March 1950, which has never been done since for United?

13. What record did Jeff Whitefoot set, at the time, when he made his senior United debut against Portsmouth in April 1950?

14. Who was emerging as the new chief scout at United at the time (succeeding Louis Rocca), among whose earliest of many discoveries was Whitefoot?

15. Who was the strapping half-back (Welsh-sounding but Barnsley-born) drafted in at the age of 17 for a debut in October 1950 against Sheffield Wednesday, having come through the junior ranks, who would come of age later in the decade during the club's back-to-back title wins?

16. After being trialled as an innovation at United training ground The Cliff as early as January 1951 – long before first being used in the Football League in February 1956 – about what bright idea was Matt Busby talking when he said the following? "I think this is the way that football will be played in the future. It gives practically everyone the chance to watch midweek matches."

17. What two-word nickname was used in print for the earliest known time in a *Daily Mirror* article on 3 March 1951, referring to the crop of exciting young players emerging at United?

18. Who was the right-winger Busby signed from Birmingham City ahead of the 1951/52 season to succeed the departed Jimmy Delaney?

19. Who was the Manchester-born player and future captain who made his senior debut at left-back – having been switched to that position from further forward – against Liverpool in November 1951?

20. After being switched temporarily back to left-wing for a spell for the crucial run-in to the 1951/52 title, the same player proceeded to score in four consecutive April matches – against Liverpool, Blackpool, and in two games against which Lancashire rival?

21. United clinched the 1951/52 Division One league title in the last game of the season, triumphing emphatically 6-1 over which club, who were their only remaining contenders in second place before kick-off?

22. Jack Rowley had broken his own record to set a new club best for number of league goals scored in a season by the end of 1951/52 – how many?

23. The 1952/53 season was Johnny Carey's last as a player, after which he left to become manager of Blackburn Rovers. What was unusual about one of Carey's final appearances, against Sunderland in February 1953, underlining his versatility?

24. In May 1953, United – by now bristling with young talent – reached the final of the newly established FA Youth Cup. Which team did they play in the final, winning 9-3 on aggregate after a 7-1 triumph in the first leg at Old Trafford?

25. Who did Busby choose to succeed Carey as captain for the 1953/54 season, which would prove to be his tenth and final campaign as a United player, and finished early with a transfer to Bury in February 1954?

26. Who became the next Manchester United captain after that, another experienced player who would bow out towards the end of the 1954/55 season with 391 United appearances to his name, to become player-manager of Grimsby Town?

27. In November 1954, the latest homegrown youngster to graduate to a first-team debut was Albert Scanlon, in a 2-1 win over Arsenal. Which former United player of the Busby era, also a winger, was Scanlon's uncle?

28. Who was the young Irish inside-forward – spotted by United's scout in Ireland Billy Behan, playing for Home Farm in his native Dublin – who made his senior debut in March 1955 against Preston North End? He would score in his second game one week later and go on to register an impressive scoring ratio of 52 goals in 98 matches.

29. In April 1955, away at Newcastle United, a 19-year-old homegrown player took to the field for the first time, playing right-wing that day but to make his mark as an outstanding inside-forward over the next nine seasons, scoring 179 goals in 293 games in total. Who?

30. United finished fifth in the league in 1954/55, but who did they beat 2-1 on the final day of the season despite that side having been crowned league champions for the first time?

31. Who had taken over as United captain come the start of the 1955/56 season, another strong and respected character but this time a man in his mid-twenties rather than in his thirties?

32. Who was the long-serving goalkeeper who played the last of his 212 senior United games in October 1955 against Huddersfield Town (he'd later return to the club as a trainer)?

33. Who was the Salford lad and product of the youth system who came through to make a senior debut, aged 19, against Bolton in November 1955? He'd become a crowd favourite and earn the nickname 'Snakehips' for his deceptive body swerve.

34. A 2-1 comeback win over which side, who finished runners-up, three games from the end of the season guaranteed United the 1955/56 league title (by a wide margin)?

35. Who finished United's top scorer in that triumphant 1955/56 campaign, with 25 goals?

36. And who was the one player to play in all 43 matches of a campaign in which he fully flourished, having featured only 22 times in the four previous seasons since a debut in 1950?

37. In United's first appearance in the European Cup, which Spanish side did they face in the European Cup quarter-final, a team who were overcome after a rousing 3-0 second-leg victory at Maine Road?

38. While going on an exciting run in Europe, United also retained the English league crown, making it back-to-back titles. Which London club were runners-up to United this time?

39. Goalkeeper David Gaskell made history for two different reasons when he played in the Charity Shield match on 24 October 1956. Why?

40. And which rival club, winners of the 1956 FA Cup, did we face in that Charity Shield match?

41. An Englishman topped the club's overall scoring charts in 1956/57 with 34 goals, but who was the Irishman who scored most goals in the league, with 26?

42. The same player kicked off the 1957/58 season in style with a 10-minute hat-trick at Leicester City to beat the Foxes 3-0. What was the name of the Leicester ground at that time?

43. Who was the future United striker who scored against the Reds both home and away for Arsenal during 1957/58?

44. Which Irish side were swatted away 9-3 on aggregate in the preliminary round of that season's European Cup?

45. In December 1957, a Northern Irish goalkeeper made his United debut against Leicester City, having arrived from Doncaster for a record fee, and would go on to play 247 games for the club. Who?

46. On 1 February 1958, United played out a famous nine-goal thriller against Arsenal at Highbury. What was the scoreline?

47. Who took over managerial duties at the club in the aftermath of the Munich Air Disaster, while Matt Busby was recovering in hospital in Germany?

48. United's first game after the disaster was an FA Cup tie against which side at Old Trafford?

49. As United began to rebuild, they finished seventh in the league table in the 1958/59 season. Which Munich survivor set a new club record for most goals scored in a season that campaign, a mark of 32 still standing as of April 2022?

50. United's final game of the 1950s, a decade of both triumph and tragedy, was a happy endorsement of the former with an emphatic 4-1 win over the team that would win that season's title – who?

THE 1960s

An unforgettable decade that saw the Reds reach Europe's pinnacle

1. Which player who signed for United in January 1960 later had a long and successful spell as Jack Charlton's assistant with the Republic of Ireland international team?

2. In 1959/60 Dennis Viollet scored more league goals in a single season than any other United player in history – a record that still stands to this day. How many league goals did he score in that epic campaign?

3. Which Irishman, who went on win the European Cup with the Reds, signed for United in April 1960, arriving from Dublin side Shelbourne?

4. Name the United legend, born in Collyhurst, north Manchester, who made his debut for the club in October 1960 against Bolton Wanderers?

5. In 1961, a 15-year-old George Best was given a trial at United. What was the name of the Belfast scout who discovered him and who messaged Matt Busby with the words: 'I think I've found you a genius'?

6. United's big signing in the summer of 1961 was Scottish forward David Herd. Which rival club did we buy him from?

7. Goalkeeping duties in 1961/62 were shared out across three players – Ronnie Briggs, David Gaskell and Harry Gregg. Which 'keeper made the most appearances in this season?

8. In January 1962, Dennis Viollet left United in a surprise move, and went on to achieve further legend status with his new club based around 50 miles down the road from Manchester. Name the club he moved to.

9. Why didn't United play a match between 26 December 1962 and 23 February 1963?

10. Which player did United sign from Celtic on 6 February 1963?

11. Against Nottingham Forest in May 1963, an 18-year-old made his debut for United, going down in history as the club's first ever black player. What was his name?

12. Midfielder Johnny Giles controversially left United in the summer of 1963 to sign for which rival team?

13. And which member of the United squad was Johnny Giles's brother-in-law?

14. The Reds' curtain-raising match of the 1963/64 season was a Charity Shield defeat to which North West team, who had won the 1962/63 Division One title?

15. How old was George Best when he made his debut in 1963?

16. Why is the 4-1 win over West Brom in January 1964 a landmark match for the club?

17. Which United player signed for Liverpool in April 1964, making him, to date, the last player to move directly between the two clubs?

18. In 1964, George Best was part of United's FA Youth Cup-winning squad. How many other players who won the Youth Cup that year also picked up European Cup-winning medals in 1968?

19. Who did United play in that 1964 FA Youth Cup final?

20. United won the title in 1965 for the first time since the Babes era. Four players played all 42 league games in that season, with three of those going on to win the European Cup in 1968. Name the latter three.

21. That 1965 title was ultimately decided by which unusual method?

22. Who became Manchester United chairman in June 1965, a role later held by his son?

23. Which stand was rebuilt in advance of Old Trafford hosting matches in the 1966 World Cup?

24. Bobby Charlton and Nobby Stiles were famously stars of England's triumphant World Cup-winning team in 1966. Which other United player appeared for England during the tournament?

25. In 1966, Alex Stepney signed for the Reds for a world-record fee for a goalkeeper. Which club did he leave to join United?

26. And which future United manager sold Stepney to the Reds?

27. What is the name of the Scottish forward who made his United debut in May 1966, and went on to have a long association with the club's Academy as well as a spell as Sir Alex Ferguson's assistant?

28. Which United legend left the club for Stoke City in December 1966, having made 247 appearances since his arrival in 1957?

29. Which star player broke his leg in March 1967, ruling him out of United's title-winning run-in?

30. And what was the name of the promising young player who broke into the first team in 1966/67, but suffered terrible injuries in a car crash which sadly cut short his playing career?

31. The Reds clinched the 1967 Division One title with a famous 6-1 victory away to which side?

32. Which team finished second to United in the 1967 title chase?

33. Denis Law was top scorer in the 1966/67 season, with 25 goals in all competitions. But who was second-top, with 18?

34. United won the Division One title in 1965 and 1967. Which team had won the title in each preceding season?

35. Which former United captain ended his playing career in 1967 and left the Reds to become manager of Coventry City?

36. The 1967 Charity Shield was a 3-3 draw between United and FA Cup holders Tottenham. What was unusual about Spurs' second goal in that match?

37. Which United player – who would go on to coach both Manchester clubs – made his debut in that Charity Shield game against Spurs?

38. United almost won the 1968 Division One title on the back of the previous year's success, finishing just two points behind which team?

39. Who was named the Football Writers' Association Footballer of the Year in 1968?

40. In the 1967/68 season, five United players scored ten or more goals across all competitions – name them.

41. Name the Scottish winger who moved to United from Burnley in August 1968.

42. Which Argentinian side did United play in a famously bad-tempered Intercontinental Cup final in 1968?

43. A future United player's father scored for the South American side in that tie. Name that player who signed for the Reds in July 2001.

44. Who was named the new United manager in June 1969?

45. Which club legend made his last appearance for the club in August 1969, at the age of 37, against Southampton?

46. Which season in the 1960s saw Best, Law and Charlton score a remarkable 71 goals between them, their highest cumulative total in a single campaign?

47. What was United's lowest final league position in the 1960s?

48. How many times did United compete in the Charity Shield in the 1960s?

49. Between the 1960/61 and 1969/70 campaigns, which player was top scorer for the season most often?

50. Not including our two shared Charity Shields, how many senior trophies did United win during the 1960s?

THE 1970s

Relegation, promotion and a glorious afternoon at Wembley

1. Manchester United won the 1969/70 FA Cup third-place play-off 2-0 at Highbury against a club who we also faced in the 2007 FA Cup semi-final. Can you name this team?

2. Three players scored two goals each in United's 7-0 Division One hammering of West Bromwich Albion at Old Trafford on 8 April 1970, but can you name any one of the three?

3. Whose short spell as the manager of United ended on 29 December 1970?

4. At the end of the 1970/71 season, a legendary Scottish international, who later enjoyed a long spell as a co-commentator for MUTV, hung up his boots. Who was it?

5. During the decade, Manchester United appointed their first, and to date only, Irish manager in the club's history. Name him.

6. In November 1971, United signed a trainee who played 248 games for the club and made 73 appearances for Northern Ireland. He played for and managed Rangers (caretaker in 2018), but can you identify this right-back?

7. Which club did Sammy McIlroy make his Manchester United debut against, scoring in a 3-3 away draw in the First Division on 6 November 1971?

8. When United were forced to play their first two home games of the 1971/72 First Division season away from Old Trafford, two separate venues were used. Can you name either one of the two grounds they played these games?

9. Can you name the 'Town' John Aston Jnr signed for when he left Old Trafford in July 1972 in a £30,000 move?

10. In December 1972, Manchester United signed a player from Arsenal who went on to manage the Gunners to First Division championship titles in 1988/89 and 1990/91. Can you name him?

11. United paid Celtic £200,00 for this forward in January 1973. He went on to win an FA Cup winners' medal with the Reds in the 1977. Identify this diminutive, livewire player.

12. A United icon left the club at the end of the 1972/73 season, having spent 17 years at Old Trafford. Name this future director of the club.

13. On 15 September 1973, he made his debut for Manchester United, coming on as a substitute for Jim Holton in a 3-1 Division One win over West Ham United. Name him and his brother who also played for United in that game.

14. In December 1973, this United forward retired due to injury. His double-barrelled surname is a combination of a synonym for tale and the surname of the captain of England's 1966 World Cup winners. Who is he?

15. He joined Manchester United from Brentford for £55,000 in December 1973, and was later assistant manager at Arsenal alongside a United team-mate – who is he?

16. United defeated 'The Pilgrims' 1-0 at Old Trafford in the third round of the 1973/74 FA Cup. Name the opposition.

17. United were relegated at the end of the 1973/74 First Division season, losing at home to Manchester City in our final home game of the campaign. The Blues won that derby 1-0 – who scored the only goal of the game?

18. In season 1973/74, United's penalty taker was a goalkeeper who scored twice from the spot, but do you know who he is?

19. Name the Northern Ireland international midfielder who was the club's leading goalscorer in the First Division in 1973/74 with only six goals.

20. In August 1974, United sold one of our 1968 European Cup winners to Arsenal for £40,000. Can you name this player who went on to lift a second European Cup plus a First Division championship title, Charity Shield, and the European Super Cup with another English side during his career?

21. Which United defender who won the Second Division in 1974/75 also played county cricket for Yorkshire – and whose son represented England at cricket?

22. When United won the Division Two title in 1974/75, which famous club were also promoted back into the top-flight by finishing runners-up in the Second Division?

23. In December 1975, United sold this Republic of Ireland international midfielder to West Bromwich Albion. He joined United in January 1973, a £30,000 purchase from Bohemians, but can you name this player whose first and last name both begin with the letter 'M'?

24. What was the lowest position in the table occupied by United in 1975/76, their first season back in the First Division, having won the Second Division the previous season?

25. United lost the 1976 FA Cup final to a Second Division team thanks to a Bobby Stokes goal. Name this south-coast club.

26. Name the former United forward – recruited from Wolves in 1974 – who played against the Reds in the 1976 FA Cup final.

27. This Republic of Ireland international goalkeeper was the back-up to Alex Stepney in 1975/76. Name him.

28. In season 1975/76, four Northern Ireland internationals played for Manchester United. How many can you name?

29. This England international forward ended the 1975/76 season as the club's top scorer in the First Division with 13 goals, but do you know who he is?

30. In season 1975/76, the captain of Manchester United played in all 42 of their First Division championship games. Name this superb Scottish international centre-half.

31. And who is the other Scottish international centre-half who left Old Trafford in October 1976 and joined Sunderland in a £64,000 transfer deal?

32. This 'United' were thrashed 7-2 at Old Trafford in the fourth round of the 1976/77 League Cup, but ended the First Division season one place higher than the Reds in fifth place. Name them.

33. In November 1976, United paid Stoke City £111,000 for a forward who went on to become a fans' favourite and who scored in the 1977 FA Cup final. Name him.

34. Name either of the two players who ended the 1976/77 season as the club's joint-top goalscorers in the First Division with 15 goals apiece.

35. Who replaced Tommy Docherty as the manager of Manchester United on 14 July 1977?

36. Name the Portuguese side who defeated United 6-5 on aggregate in the second round of the 1977/78 European Cup Winners' Cup.

37. In January 1978, Manchester United signed a goalkeeper from Wits University, Johannesburg, South Africa, but do you know who he is?

38. When United bought this striker in January 1978 for £350,000, it set a new record transfer fee between two English clubs. Can you name the player – nicknamed 'Jaws' – United signed and the team he was purchased from?

39. This former star of Gaelic football joined Manchester United in February 1978 at the age of 21 – can you name the Irish defender who played a big part in United's 1980s story?

40. When he signed for United in February 1978, in a £495,000 transfer, it was a record British transfer fee for a defender. Name this former Leeds United and Scotland centre-half.

41. Nicknamed 'Merlin', this left winger departed United in April 1978 and teamed up once again with his former United manager Tommy Docherty at Derby County. Can you Identify him?

42. Which Scottish club did defender Alex Forsyth sign for in August 1978, after playing 119 games for United?

43. In November 1978, United signed a flying winger from Wrexham, a Welsh international who scored a famous free-kick for Wrexham in the 1991/92 FA Cup to help knock Arsenal out of the competition. Who is he?

44. Can you name the club who defeated United 3-2 in a dramatic 1979 FA Cup final?

45. Manchester United paid a club-record fee for this England international midfielder in August 1979. Name him and the club he was purchased from.

46. In August 1979, this Northern Ireland international midfielder left United for Queens Park Rangers in a £200,000 transfer – can you name him?

47. He was the last player to leave Manchester United in the 1970s, departing in August 1979 in a £220,000 transfer. Name this club legend who scored in the 1977 FA Cup final.

48. This Scottish international striker, whose first and last name both begin with the same letter, ended the 1979/80 season as the club's leading goalscorer with 13 goals in all competitions. Name him.

49. What position did Manchester United finish in the 1979/80 First Division?

50. In season 1979/80, United were knocked out of the FA Cup by a club who won at least one major trophy in each of the six decades from the 1950s to 2000s, an achievement only matched by United, but who are they?

THE 1980s

Trophies delivered, heroes emerge and a certain Scot arrives

1. Manchester United signed the club's first ever overseas player in January 1980, paying Red Star Belgrade £350,000 for their Yugoslavian international centre-half. Name him.

2. On 1 March 1980, United lost 6-0 away to Ipswich Town in the First Division, but can you name the United goalkeeper who saved three penalties in the game?

3. On 29 May 1980, United signed a trainee striker who went on to enjoy two spells at Old Trafford during his illustrious career. Name this legend.

4. In what position did United end the 1980/81 First Division season?

5. Joe Jordan ended the 1980/81 season as the club's leading First Division scorer with 15 goals, but can you name his fellow Scot who scored nine league goals for United during the campaign?

6. In season 1980/81, United were knocked out of the UEFA Cup by a Polish side with the letter 'z' in the first and second name of their club name. Who are they?

7. Can you name the reigning European Cup holders who defeated United 1-0 in the fourth round of the 1980/81 FA Cup?

8. Only two players appeared in all 42 of United's 1980/81 First Division games. Steve Coppell was one of them, but which Scottish international left-back was the other ever-present?

9. On 13 September 1980, United defeated this 'City' 5-0 at Old Trafford in the First Division. Name the opposition or any two of United's four goalscorers in that game.

10. During the 1980/81 season, United drew 3-3 home and away with Aston Villa, but which Northern Ireland international scored a penalty for United in both games?

11. In December 1980, Jimmy Greenhoff left Old Trafford. The United legend moved to a club based in a famous railway town in Cheshire, but who are they?

12. Who succeeded Dave Sexton as the manager of United prior to the start of the 1981/82 season, and which club did he leave to take up his position at Old Trafford?

13. In what position in the First Division did United finish the 1981/82 season?

14. Can you name the striker Manchester United paid £950,000 for in August 1981, and the London team they bought him from?

15. United were knocked out of the 1981/82 FA Cup in the third round by a club who were managed by a future England manager, and who had a famous chairman. Name the club, their manager and the chairman.

16. Born in Glasgow, this striker made 16 appearances for United in 1981/82 and scored two goals. In July 1984, he was sold to Portsmouth for £85,000. Can you identify this player?

17. In 1981/82, United lost 2-1 both home and away in the First Division to the reigning UEFA Cup holders. Name this club and their manager, who was appointed England boss on 7 July 1982.

18. Name the two players who joined United from West Bromwich Albion during the 1981/82 season.

19. In October 1980, United paid £1.25 million for this striker who was prolific for his previous club but could not reproduce the same rate of goals-per-game when he moved to Old Trafford. Name him.

20. In summer 1981, United bought a defender from Everton and sold a midfielder to the same club. Name either player.

21. On 27 April 1982, Manchester United paid St. Patrick's Athletic £80,000 for a player who went on to become an FA Cup winner in 1985, and who remains a cult hero with Manchester United fans. Name this Irish legend.

22. United reached the 1982 FA Youth Cup final, losing over two legs to Watford. Name the two players who scored in that final and went on to achieve legend status at the club.

23. He made his debut for United on the opening day of the 1982/83 season. Name this midfielder, who was the first Dutch player to play for United, and the club he signed from?

24. With 14 goals in the First Division and 19 in all competitions, he was the club's leading goalscorer in 1982/83, but can you name him?

25. In 1982/83, United reached the League Cup final for the first time but lost 2-1 after extra-time at Wembley. Can you name the team they lost to or United's goalscorer?

26. In October 1983, a United legend was forced to retire through injury. This skilful winger won the FA Cup with the Reds in 1977, but do you know his name?

27. In September 1982, United bought a player from Vancouver Whitecaps for £250,000. He played just one game for the Reds but went on to win the First Division twice and the FA Cup with another team. Name him and the club he won these trophies with.

28. United were FA Cup holders entering the 1983/84 season, but were sensationally knocked out in the third round by a south-coast club, losing 2-0 at Dean Court. Which club beat us and who was the boss of this Third Division side, someone who later managed Tottenham Hotspur in the Premier League?

29. Can you name the iconic player who scored both goals for United when we defeated Liverpool 2-0 at Wembley in the 1983 Charity Shield?

30. Name the United defender who played 456 games for the Reds after arriving at Old Trafford on 29 February 1972, and who moved to Oldham Athletic in August 1983 on a free transfer?

31. In November 1983, United signed a winger on loan from Tottenham, and in 1999 he was awarded an OBE for his services to football. In 2020/21, he was the BBC's lead pundit on their Saturday '*Final Score*' programme. Name him.

32. In the third round of the 1983/84 League Cup, Manchester United won 2-0 away at Layer Road in Essex to a 'United' side nicknamed 'The U's'. Name them.

33. Name the two wingers who made their debut for United on 25 August 1984, in the opening game of the First Division season, a 1-1 draw with Watford at Old Trafford.

34. This full-back was born in Accrington, Lancashire, and won the FA Cup with United in 1983, playing in the final and the replay, and won a second FA Cup winners' medal with the club in 1985. He left Old Trafford at the start of the 1990/91 season to join Blackburn Rovers. Who is this ex-England international?

35. Prior to the start of the 1984/85 season, Ray Wilkins left Old Trafford after five years with the Reds. Can you name the Italian club he moved to?

36. Who was the United's leading goalscorer in across 1984/85, with 16 goals in the league and 24 goals in all competitions?

37. During the 1984/85 season, three Republic of Ireland internationals played for United, but can you name this famous trio of stars?

38. That same season, 1984/85, a Scottish international striker scored nine goals for United in 26 appearances, but can you name this future radio personality?

39. United won the opening 10 games of the 1985/86 First Division season, but can you identify the side that ended our winning run on 5 October 1985, drawing 1-1 at Kenilworth Road?

40. Name the player United paid Nottingham Forest £570,000 for on 24 March 1986, and who was our top scorer in the 1986/87 First Division season.

41. On 4 November 1986, United lost 4-1 away in a League Cup third-round replay, resulting in manager Ron Atkinson being sacked. Can you name the team who eliminated United?

42. This new signing was the club's leading scorer in 1987/88 with 24 goals in the First Division and 31 in all competitions. Name him and the Scottish club he was bought from for £850,000.

43. That player was joined at the club by Viv Anderson. From which club did we sign that England international?

44. On 17 December 1987, United paid £825,000 for an English centre-half from a fellow First Division club. Can you name this player and the club he was signed from?

45. Name this player who won two Scottish Premier League titles, four Scottish FA Cups and the European Cup Winners' Cup during Alex Ferguson's reign as manager of Aberdeen and who signed for United on 14 May 1988 in a £450,000 deal.

46. Can you name the Scottish midfielder who United signed as a trainee on 1 July 1988, and who went on to win the inaugural Premier League title with the club |in 1992/93?

47. What was United's league position at the end of the 1988/89 season?

48. On 18 September 1989, this Southampton player was Alex Ferguson's last signing of the decade, but can you name the speedy winger?

49. Which two players ended up joint-top scorers in the 1988/89 season, with 16 goals each?

50. How many games did United play at Wembley Stadium during the 1980s?

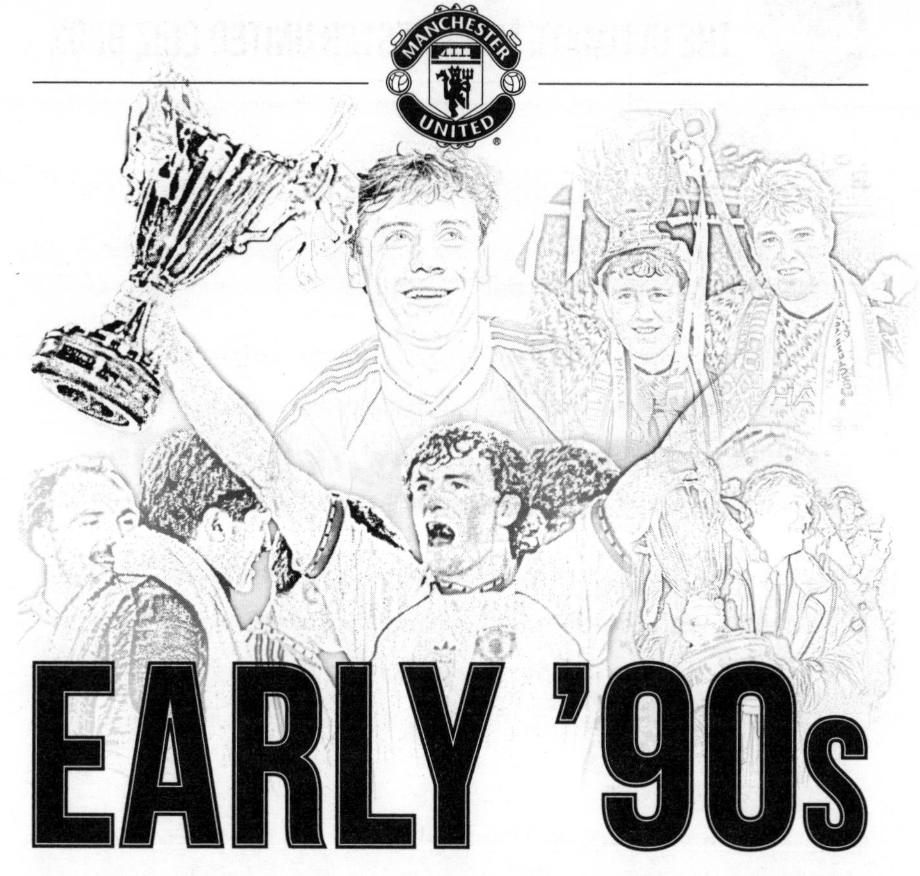

EARLY '90s

European success returns, with the club on the cusp of a golden era

1. United's first goal of the 1990s was scored in a famous FA Cup third-round 1-0 win away to Nottingham Forest. Who scored this vital goal?

2. At the end of the 1989/90 season, who was United's leading goalscorer when recording 13 goals in the league and 15 goals in all competitions?

3. He played in the 1990 FA Cup final for United but was dropped for the replay. Can you name this Scottish international keeper?

4. United had two players in England's 1990 World Cup squad – can you name them?

5. One of those – England's captain – was injured in the second World Cup group-stage game and missed the rest of the tournament. Against which country did that injury happen?

6. Name the reigning First Division champions who United shared the 1990 Charity Shield with following a 1-1 draw at Wembley Stadium.

7. United defeated Pecsi Munkas both home and away in the first round of the 1990/91 European Cup Winners' Cup. Can you name the East European country Pecsi Munkas are from?

8. On 20 October 1990, the eventual 1990/91 Division One champions defeated United 1-0 at Old Trafford in the league. During the game, a mass brawl ensued between players from both sides, resulting in United being deducted one point and the away team being deducted two points. Name the visitors.

9. Name the 'City' who have never won the FA Cup or the First Division/Premier League, but knocked United out of the 1990/91 FA Cup with a 2-1 home victory in the fifth round?

10. Name the winger United signed on 26 March 1991 in a £650,000 transfer from Shakhtar Donetsk.

11. In the 1990/91 League Cup, United eliminated three teams who they had previously played in an FA Cup final. Can you name any two of the three and the years prior to 1991 in which United played them in the FA Cup final?

12. What was United's final league position in the 1990/91 season?

13. Forwards Mark Hughes and Brian McClair were joint-top goalscorers in the 1990/91 season with 21 goals each, but which player was the unlikely source of an incredible 19 goals in all competitions in this campaign?

14. A team whose club nickname is a bird, defeated United in the 1991 League Cup final. Can you name the bird and the Yorkshire-based team?

15. Prior to the start of the 1991/92 season, Alex Ferguson signed a full-back whose surname is the same as the fictional character who served as butler and chauffeur to Lady Penelope in the TV series *Thunderbirds*. Name this player.

16. On 5 August 1991, United played a friendly against a Scottish Premier League side who won the European Cup Winners' Cup in 1982/83. Can you identify this side?

17. The very next day, on 6 August, United signed a player who went on to win the 1992 European Championship with his country. Name him.

18. The 1991/92 season was the last ever English First Division campaign, with the Premier League era soon to begin. In what position did United finish in the league?

19. After breaking into the United first-team in 1990/91, he was named the 1991/92 PFA Young Player of the Year. Who is he?

20. Can you name the former winners of the European Cup who United defeated 1-0 in the 1992 League Cup final?

21. United famously won the FA Youth Cup in 1992. Who were the opposition in that match?

22. Name the members of that squad went on to win a Champions League winners' medal in 1999.

23. What is the name of the legendary coach who managed that Youth Cup-winning team?

24. What was the name of the midfielder who won a Youth Cup medal in 1992 who never made a first-team appearance for United, but won a League Cup winners' medal with Leicester City in 2000?

25. Our last ever match in the old Division One in May 1992 saw United win 3-1 at Old Trafford, with our opponent's goal scored by their star striker in his last game before leaving to play for a club in Japan. Name our opponents and their departing striker.

THE PREMIER LEAGUE ERA

A top-flight transformation and a new age of United dominance

1992/93

1. The first ever goal in the history of the Premier League was scored against United – by which player, for which club?

2. Who captained United in our first ever PL game?

3. Less well-remembered is United's first ever Premier League opponents at Old Trafford, who served up a shock 3-0 win. Who defeated us on that August day?

4. United's first Premier League win came with a 1-0 victory away at Southampton. Which player scored his first ever United goal to secure the points?

5. Our league matches against Liverpool saw a 2-2 draw at Old Trafford and a 2-1 win at Anfield. Which player scored three of our four goals in those games?

6. What was unusual about the Old Trafford stadium for the majority of the 1992/93 season?

7. Which teams finished second and third to United in the table?

8. United were handed the title when the second-placed team lost at home to which North West side?

9. Which other North West side were the opposition when United lifted the PL trophy in our penultimate game of the season?

10. And the final victory party took place in our last game of the season, against which London side?

11. Who scored our final goal in that 2-1 win away in London?

12. How many points clear were United at the top of the table by the end of the season?

13. How many years had it been since United had last won the top-flight title?

14. David Beckham, Nicky Butt and Gary Neville all made their United debuts in the 1992/93 season, but only one did so in the Premier League. Which one?

15. Four Reds played all 42 games in this Premier League campaign – how many of them can you name?

1993/94

1. Which player became the most expensive in British football history at the time when he signed for Manchester United in July 1993?

2. United's campaign curtain-raiser was the Charity Shield at Wembley. Which team did the Reds face that day?

3. Who did United kick off the defence of their Premier League crown against?

4. The Reds were 2-0 down at half-time in the first derby of the season. Which Man City striker scored both those goals?

5. And what was the final score in that Maine Road match in November?

6. There was a dramatic New Year clash between United and Liverpool at Anfield on 4 January. What was the final score?

7. How many goals did Eric Cantona score against Man City in the two league games in 1993/94?

8. Peter Schmeichel played 40 of the 42 PL matches this season. Which goalkeeper was picked for those two other games?

9. Can you name the three Scotsmen who played in the Premier League for United this season?

10. Name the team who spent their one season in the Premier League in 1993/94 – United beat them 4-2 at Old Trafford but drew 2-2 away at their place.

11. Who finished second in the Premier League this season?

12. Two defenders made the joint-most appearances for United in all comps this season, with 62 matches – name them.

13. Which United star was voted the PFA Player of the Year?

14. United sealed the league and Cup double for the first time in our history. Who was the last club before this season to achieve that feat?

15. The legendary Bryan Robson left at the end of the season, to become player-manager of which club?

1994/95

1. Which striker smashed a trademark cracker against QPR to get the season up and running?

2. Which of our favourite sons scored on his Premier League debut in the shock 3-2 defeat to Ipswich Town?

3. What was the final score in a thrilling win against Blackburn Rovers at Ewood Park in October?

4. Andrei Kanchelskis scored a hat-trick in the Manchester derby, the first Red to do so in a game against City since which Scottish forward claimed a treble in 1960?

5. Which goalkeeper made his senior United debut in the 3-0 win over Crystal Palace at Old Trafford in November?

6. Which member of the Class of '92 netted his maiden first-team goal in the New Year's Eve fixture, against Southampton?

7. Which United youngster moved to Newcastle in part-exchange when the Reds secured the shock signing of Andy Cole?

8. Eric Cantona got the winner in the title clash with Blackburn when Ryan Giggs robbed which future Red of the ball?

9. Three days later, Cantona made headline news when he was sent off (before attacking a fan) against which club?

10. How many goals did Andy Cole score against Ipswich in the 9-0 victory?

11. Which defender hit the only goal of the home game against Sheffield Wednesday to keep our title hopes alive?

12. The surname of Southampton's scorer in the final league game at Old Trafford had strong Red connections. Who was it?

13. Alex Ferguson's side conceded remarkably few goals at home in the league – how many did we let in, in total?

14. Name the goalkeeper who had probably the game of his life to deny United during an agonising final-day draw at West Ham?

15. Who was United's top Premier League scorer in this season, the only campaign when he managed the feat?

1995/96

1. Who scored United's opening goal of the season, a consolation in the 3-1 away defeat to Aston Villa on August 19?

2. Which former Liverpool star famously remarked after that game that 'you can't win anything with kids'?

3. Eric Cantona made his comeback from suspension in the 2-2 draw with Liverpool, scoring a penalty, but who did he assist for the opening goal?

4. Ryan Giggs scored after only 15 seconds in a 4-1 home victory over which side?

5. Just after Christmas, United won a vital game 2-0 against leaders Newcastle. Andy Cole netted against his former club but who else got on the scoresheet?

6. Name the French defender who made two appearances for the club, against QPR and Tottenham Hotspur, over the festive period.

7. United enjoyed a fine away day at Bolton Wanderers in February but what was the final score?

8. Eric Cantona volleyed the priceless goal in the vital 1-0 win at Newcastle but who provided the assist for the strike?

9. It sparked a scoring streak of how many consecutive Premier League games for the Frenchman?

10. Andy Cole found the net in the key 3-2 derby triumph at Manchester City but which shirt number did he wear in his first full season at Old Trafford?

11. In April, who inflicted the Reds' first league defeat since New Year's Day, with Ryan Giggs getting the consolation in a 3-1 loss?

12. Roy Keane finally broke 10-man Leeds' stubborn resistance at Old Trafford but what was unusual about the goal?

13. Kevin Keegan's infamous rant in the run-in came after Alex Ferguson referenced an upcoming testimonial between Newcastle and Nottingham Forest for which player?

14. Which colour kit did United wear for the title-clinching final league game of the season at Middlesbrough?

15. It was one of the all-time classic Premier League title races but how many points did the Reds ultimately win by?

1996/97

1. What was special about United's third goal in the opening-day win over Wimbledon?

2. The Reds' first two home fixtures of the season, against Everton and Blackburn Rovers, ended 2-2. Which summer signing scored in both games?

3. Which team were beaten 5-0 at Old Trafford, in United's biggest league win of the season?

4. Name the goalkeeper who made his debut when the Reds travelled to Villa Park.

5. Which two outfield players joined Peter Schmeichel in making 36 Premier League appearances out of a possible 38?

6. At which two away grounds did United win 4-0?

7. Which Midlands club had a nightmare start at Old Trafford by scoring two own goals in the first five minutes?

8. What was the final score in both the Reds' home and away draws with Aston Villa?

9. How many goals did United concede in total, when losing back-to-back away games to Newcastle United and Southampton in October?

10. Which side did United share 10 goals with by drawing 2-2 away and 3-3 at home?

11. Whose famous old ground did the Reds visit for the last time in the 1996/97 season?

12. Which defender netted a double in the thrilling 3-1 away win over Liverpool?

13. Who scored his last goal for the club when United beat Blackburn 3-2 in April 1997?

14. Which player finished the season as United's top Premier League scorer with 18 goals?

15. The Premier League trophy was presented after the final home game against West Ham, but who lifted it as United's captain?

1997/98

1. How many consecutive clean sheets did United keep in the Premier League at the start of 1997/98, before finally conceding a goal on 13 September?

2. Which former United player scored for the visitors when Chelsea drew 2-2 at Old Trafford?

3. How many goals in total did the Reds score in back-to-back thrashings of Barnsley and Sheffield Wednesday?

4. Who scored a hat-trick against Barnsley?

5. Finally on the Barnsley fixture, which United Academy graduate came off the bench to make his senior debut?

6. True or false? The players on the scoresheet when United defeated Liverpool 3-1 at Anfield were all England internationals.

7. Which club did the Reds defeat 1-0 away, four days before Christmas, with a goal from Andy Cole?

8. United's best winning streak of the campaign started on 22 November and ended on 28 December. How many league victories in a row did the Reds achieve in that spell?

9. Which ex-Red helped to end that run, by scoring a late penalty in Coventry City's shock 3-2 triumph?

10. How many Norwegian players made Premier League appearances for United in 1997/98?

11. At which ground did United play two away league games in this season?

12. True or false? The Reds earned more points as runners-up in 1997/98 than as champions in 1996/97.

13. Andy Cole was United's top league scorer with 15 goals but which two players finished second in the list with nine strikes apiece?

14. Which venue did the Reds visit for the first and so far only time in the Premier League during this campaign?

15. United only netted two penalties in the league. Who converted both of them?

1998/99

1. The Reds began the 1998/99 Premier League season at home to Leicester City. David Beckham dramatically secured a 2-2 draw in injury-time, but which United forward earlier halved the deficit?

2. Dwight Yorke made his debut in the Reds' second game of the league season, against which London side?

3. During the course of the 1998/99 league campaign, how many own goals were scored in United's favour?

4. Which Reds veteran announced during the season that 1998/99 would be his final campaign at the club?

5. At which stadium did strike partners Andy Cole and Dwight Yorke both score in the same game for the first time?

6. United suffered three league defeats all season – against which teams?

7. In December, the Reds played six Premier League games, against Aston Villa, Tottenham, Chelsea (twice), Middlesbrough, Nottingham Forest. How many of the 18 points available were won?

8. Which player scored the only brace of his Reds career in Boxing Day's home win over Nottingham Forest?

9. What unusual event delayed kick-off in United's first league game of 1999: the 4-1 home win over West Ham?

10. Which first-team squad member joined Celta Vigo on loan in early 1999?

11. Ole Gunnar Solskjaer famously scored four goals as a substitute against Nottingham Forest – which player did he replace at the City Ground?

12. United scored two penalties and conceded one during the entire league campaign. Against which team did all three conversions take place?

13. Which ex-Red was Blackburn Rovers manager when a goalless draw with United ensured their relegation to the Championship?

14. While United went up against Tottenham on the final day of the league season, which team were nearest challengers Arsenal hosting at Highbury?

15. Which substitute scored the goal which secured a 2-1 win over Spurs and regained the title?

1999/2000

1. At which stadium did Sir Alex Ferguson's reigning champions begin their title defence?

2. Andy Cole scored four goals against which of his former sides in a 5-1 August romp at Old Trafford?

3. Which new signing was named Sky Sports' Man of the Match after making his debut in a 3-2 win over Liverpool?

4. Which other new United arrival made his bow at Anfield that day?

5. In October 1999, United lost at Chelsea – a first Premier League defeat since December 1998 – by what score?

6. Which player notched his first goal for the club in Boxing Day's 4-0 win over Bradford?

7. Which team provided the opposition in the Reds' first game after the Club World Cup in Brazil?

8. Four players scored Premier League hat-tricks for United in 1999/2000 – who were they?

9. What was the score in the Reds' final ever meeting with Wimbledon, in February 2000?

10. Which player opened the scoring for West Ham in the Reds' 7-1 win at Old Trafford?

11. Who made the highest number of starts (33 of 38) for United during the league season?

12. How many goalkeepers made a Premier League appearance for United during the campaign?

13. A 3-1 win at Southampton confirmed the title retention with how many games to spare?

14. The Reds scored in all-but two of the 38 league games – against which teams did they draw a blank?

15. United ended the campaign with a long winning streak of how many successive league victories?

2000/01

1. Who did United play in the curtain-raising Charity Shield match at Wembley in August?

2. Which international goalkeeper made 44 appearances for United in his debut season following his arrival in May 2000?

3. And which goalkeeper returned to the country of his birth that summer, having made only four league appearances for United?

4. Which striker scored against his former club in the first league game of the season?

5. In September 2000, United handed out a 6-0 drubbing to which Yorkshire side?

6. In December, a Treble hero defender left United to return to his previous club. Name the player and the club.

7. Who did United beat 6-1 at Old Trafford on 25 February 2001?

8. And which player scored a hat-trick in that 6-1 win?

9. When United's goalkeeper was injured in the warm-up v Leicester in March, which teenage US-born 'keeper was called up for his one and only league appearance for United?

10. Which veteran goalkeeper then arrived on a short-term loan in March, playing two league games for the Reds?

11. It was announced in April 2001 that United had sealed the transfer of which striker in an English record deal?

12. Name the Belgrade-born midfielder who made his United debut in the final league game of the season away to Tottenham Hotspur.

13. The Reds finished 10 points clear of which team who finished runners-up in 2000/01?

14. Who was United's top goalscorer this season, and also named FWA and PFA Player of the Year?

15. Which defender made the most appearances for United this season, playing 49 games in all competitions?

2001/02

1. Why was Sir Alex Ferguson in the news in the summer of 2001?

2. Which former United player was promoted to first-team coach following the departure of Sir Alex's number two in the summer?

3. And what was the name of the departing assistant, who left to become Middlesbrough manager?

4. Which player scored on his United debut against Liverpool in the Community Shield?

5. The same player scored twice on his Old Trafford debut in our first league game of the season. Against which club?

6. Which future United striker scored twice against the Reds in that league opener?

7. Which defender was sold to Lazio in August 2001?

8. And which World Cup winner was bought to replace him?

9. One of our most memorable Premier League matches came in September 2001, when we came from behind at White Hart Lane to win 5-3. Name United's goalscorers that day.

10. It wasn't the only time we won in London by that score in '01/02. Against which other team was the 5-3 win repeated?

11. Which Treble winner moved to Everton in November 2001?

12. And Andy Cole was also on the move. Which club did he sign for in December 2001?

13. Our biggest win of the season was a 6-1 league victory in December against which club?

14. Diego Forlan arrived in January 2002. How many goals did he score for United in the 2001/02 season?

15. Arsenal sealed the title with a 1-0 win at Old Trafford in May. Which Gunners player scored the only goal of the game?

2002/03

1. Prior to the start of the 2002/03 season, United broke the British transfer record to sign which player?

2. Sir Alex Ferguson's men started the league campaign with a narrow 1-0 victory over West Brom. Which substitute scored the decisive goal – his 100th in United colours?

3. With the future of Craven Cottage uncertain, at which London ground did Fulham host United in October 2002?

4. Manchester City beat United 3-1 in November to record their first derby win of the Premier League era. But what else was notable about the game?

5. Diego Forlan's double at Anfield helped us beat Liverpool 2-1 in December. Which Liverpool goalkeeper shipped the goals?

6. The Reds then defeated reigning champions Arsenal 2-0 at Old Trafford just days later. Which player delivered a surprise Man-of-the-Match turn in central midfield?

7. Our fifth and final Premier League defeat of 2002/03 came on Boxing Day against which North East club?

8. Name the United goalkeeper that saved a penalty against Blackburn in his only league appearance, in April 2003.

9. United beat Newcastle 5-3 at Old Trafford and 6-2 at St James' Park. Which two Reds scored hat-tricks in those victories?

10. We failed to win just one of our final 10 league games – a 2-2 draw away at Arsenal. Which player headed home our equaliser in north London?

11. United were officially confirmed champions when Leeds beat Arsenal 3-2 at Highbury in May. Name the Australian that scored the Yorkshire side's winner at Highbury.

12. It was the club's eighth Premier League trophy, bringing our all-time total of top-flight titles to how many?

13. United won 2-1 at Everton on the final day of the season. Which Red scored his 85th and final goal for the club in that match?

14. Ruud van Nistelrooy led United's title charge with 25 goals. Who had the next highest tally, with 14 Premier League strikes?

15. The title would prove Roy Keane's seventh and final Premier League triumph as a United player. But how many times did he lift the trophy as captain?

2003/04

1. Carlos Queiroz left his role as assistant manager in the summer of 2003 to become head coach of which club?

2. Cristiano Ronaldo made his United debut as a substitute against Bolton on the opening day of the season. Which player did he replace in the 61st minute?

3. Which player opened the scoring in the 4-0 win over Bolton, by netting our first post-Beckham free-kick?

4. During 2003/04, Eric Djemba-Djemba became the first player to represent United from which African nation?

5. We met Wolverhampton Wanderers for the first time in a Premier League game on 27 August 2003, winning 1-0. Which former United pair featured for the visitors in that game?

6. United paid a first visit to Leicester City's new ground – now known as the King Power Stadium – during 2003/04, winning 4-1. What was the stadium called then?

7. Which Scottish Academy graduate made his Premier League debut in that game, at the age of 19?

8. Against which club did Cristiano Ronaldo score his first United goal?

9. United beat Blackburn Rovers 2-1 at Old Trafford on Saturday 22 November 2003 (a day notable for being when the England rugby team won the World Cup). Which Brazilian scored United's winner with his first Reds goal?

10. United beat City 3-1 in the first Manchester derby of the season. What did all three goals (Scholes 2, van Nistelrooy) have in common?

11. Louis Saha needed just 18 minutes to find the net on his United debut. Who were the opponents?

12. Who scored United's first-ever goal at Manchester City's Eastlands Stadium in a 4-1 defeat in March 2004?

13. 2003/04 was Gary Neville's best goalscoring season as a Red. How many of his seven United goals were scored that term?

14. Which two Reds received red cards in our final game of the season – a 2-0 win away at Villa?

15. United finished third in the Premier League – which clubs finished above us?

2004/05

1. Wayne Rooney memorably joined United that summer, but can you recall the other Premier League striker we signed ahead of the season?

2. We also captured a Paris Saint-Germain defender who became a fans' favourite: who was he?

3. It was the end of an era for Class of '92 graduate Nicky Butt, who joined which Premier League rival?

4. The season began with a defeat to which London club: Chelsea or Tottenham Hotspur?

5. Our first league goal of the season was scored by a Frenchman, in a 2-1 win over Norwich City: name him.

6. Rio Ferdinand made a long-awaited return from suspension in September, against which historic rival?

7. This will test your knowledge: which unlikely source scored a brace in that 2-1 win?

8. How many opening league games did Wayne Rooney miss with the injury he sustained at Euro 2020 – five, six or seven?

9. What was the score in October when United ended Arsenal's record-breaking 49-game unbeaten league run?

10. That feisty match against Arsenal later became known as what, following a post-match incident in the tunnel?

11. We did the double over Liverpool that season by winning 1-0 at Anfield. Who scored the winner that day?

12. What was the score following Roy Keane and Patrick Vieira's legendary bust-up in the Highbury tunnel?

13. Which unlikely goalscorer rounded off that win at Arsenal with a stunning chip?

14. Who was our top scorer in the league with 11 goals: Cristiano Ronaldo, Wayne Rooney, Louis Saha, Alan Smith or Ruud van Nistelrooy?

15. In which position did we finish the league season?

2005/06

1. True or false: summer signing Ji-sung Park became the Premier League's first South Korean player?

2. United signed two goalkeepers that summer: Edwin van der Sar from Fulham and which other stopper from Stoke City?

3. Phil Neville left for Everton after how many United appearances – 280, 380 or 480?

4. United became the first team to score 1,000 Premier League goals in October. Who scored that 1,00th goal?

5. Roy Keane's United career came to an end in November: who did he play his last game against?

6. Who scored the only goal in November's 1-0 win over rivals Chelsea at Old Trafford?

7. From which team did we sign Nemanja Vidic, whose transfer was confirmed in January 2006 following approval of his work permit and visa?

8. Patrice Evra famously made his debut, and was replaced at half-time, against which rival club?

9. In January, which defender scored in the 90th minute to earn a 1-0 win over Liverpool?

10. Two Academy graduates made Premier League debuts that season: one was Italian, the other Spanish. Who were they?

11. The great Paul Scholes was limited to 20 league appearances due to what type of temporary problem – hearing or eyesight?

12. How many consecutive wins did we register between February and April?

13. United eventually finished second in the league that season, behind which club?

14. Ruud van Nistelrooy finished with how many Premier League goals – 18, 21 or 24?

15. The PFA Team of the Year featured two Reds: Cristiano Ronaldo and which striker?

2006/07

1. Who was United's only summer signing, arriving from Tottenham in July?

2. Which shirt number did he take, and who was the last player to have worn that number?

3. Which Spanish team, who were reigning UEFA Cup champions, came to Old Trafford for a pre-season friendly in July 2006?

4. United got off to a brilliant start in the league with Wayne Rooney and Cristiano Ronaldo on form. Who were the opposition, and what was the score?

5. Which player scored against Liverpool on his 500th appearance for United?

6. And which other player scored in that 2-0 win at Old Trafford in October?

7. Loan signing Henrik Larsson scored on his United debut when we knocked Aston Villa out of the FA Cup in January, but against which team did the Swedish international register his first Premier League goal for the Reds?

8. United won 4-0 away at Spurs in February. Who ended the match in goal for the Reds?

9. The same player scored an injury-time winner at which ground that March?

10. A vital 4-2 win away at Everton moved United one step closer to the title. Two of the Reds' goals were scored by John O'Shea and Wayne Rooney – who scored the other two for United?

11. United all-but sealed the title with a 1-0 win away at Man City in May. Who got the only goal of the game?

12. The Reds were confirmed as champions when Chelsea drew 0-0 with which team?

13. Deposed champions Chelsea provided a guard of honour for the newly-crowned champions at Stamford Bridge in May. Who was the United captain and led the Reds out that day?

14. And which striker made his United debut that day in west London?

15. Which side secured their Premier League safety with a win at Old Trafford on the final day of the season, and which future Red scored the only goal of the game?

2007/08

1. Ole Gunnar Solskjaer announced his retirement from playing in August 2007. How old was he when he hung up his boots?

2. United beat FA Cup winners Chelsea in the Community Shield on penalties, after a 1-1 draw. But what was the score when the two sides met at Old Trafford in the Premier League?

3. What's the name of the Huddersfield-born Academy graduate striker who made his debut as a sub against Manchester City in August 2007?

4. And which England international midfielder also made his debut in that game following his summer transfer to United?

5. How many games did it take for champions United to win for the first time in the league this season?

6. That game – a 1-0 win at home to Spurs –saw which player score his first goal for the club?

7. What was the name of the Angolan forward who arrived in the January transfer window?

8. *Match of the Day's* Goal of the Month for January 2008 was an outstanding free-kick by Cristiano Ronaldo against which club?

9. Which goal keeper made his United debut away to Derby in March?

10. Which defender made the most appearances for United in 2007/08, with 52 matches?

11. That same player only scored one goal in 2007/08, but it was a big one. Against which team did he open the scoring in a 3-0 win at Old Trafford in March?

12. Which centre-back returned to his hometown club in May 2008, having made 23 United appearances?

13. Who scored more goals for United in all competitions in 2007/08 – Carlos Tevez or Wayne Rooney?

14. Against which team did United secure the title on the final day of the season?

15. And how many top-flight titles had United now won?

2008/09

1. Which midfielder scored in each of United's first two games of the campaign – a 1-1 draw at home to Newcastle and a 1-0 victory at Portsmouth?

2. Who made his United debut as Liverpool came from behind to beat us at Anfield in September – our first defeat to the Merseysiders in the league since 2004?

3. Samir Nasri's second goal in the 2-1 defeat at Arsenal in November 2008 would be the last United would concede in the league until February 2009. How many consecutive clean sheets did we go on to record in the top flight?

4. What was special about Cristiano Ronaldo's goal during the 5-0 victory over Stoke City in November?

5. Blackburn striker Roque Santa Cruz was the man to finally end United's record streak without conceding a goal, but which keeper did he score past?

6. Other than Liverpool – who won both meetings – and Arsenal, who were the only other side to inflict defeat on United?

7. Federico Macheda etched his name into United folklore with two late winners to keep us ahead of Liverpool in the title race. The teenager scored against Aston Villa and which other side?

8. Macheda's Villa winner is remembered particularly fondly, but can you remember who registered the assist for the goal with a precise ball into the forward's feet?

9. United trailed 2-0 at half-time to Tottenham in a key fixture at Old Trafford in late April. What was the full-time score?

10. United were confirmed as champions after a goalless draw at home in the penultimate game of the season, against who?

11. Who received the Premier League trophy when it was presented to United after that game?

12. Which Academy graduate scored our final goal of the season – and his first for the club – as a number of Reds were rested at Hull City ahead of the Champions League final three days later?

13. Can you name the three Reds to make over 30 starts during the 2008/09 top-flight campaign?

14. What was United's final Premier League points tally, as we finished four clear of Rafa Benitez's Liverpool?

15. Ronaldo was our top scorer with 18 league goals, but which rival forward pipped him to the Golden Boot after netting on the final day?

2009/10

1. Against which Midlands side did we begin our quest for an unprecedented fourth straight Premier League crown?

2. Which summer signing notched his first Reds goal during a 5-0 beating of Wigan at the DW Stadium?

3. Our meeting with Manchester City in September proved to be one of the most memorable derbies of all time, but in which minute was the winning goal scored?

4. Who was sent off at Anfield for the second consecutive season?

5. Aston Villa beat United at Old Trafford in December, but who were the only other side to escape M16 with all three points during 2009/10?

6. How many goals did Wayne Rooney contribute to January's 4-0 victory over Hull City at Old Trafford?

7. What scoring landmark did Rooney and Paul Scholes both achieve over the course of the campaign?

8. At which London stadium did we record a first-ever league win, in January 2010?

9. Which North West club held United to a 0-0 draw on their own patch in April, a result which would ultimately prove crucial in us failing to win the title?

10. What did Gary Neville do to team-mate Paul Scholes after the latter scored a late winner at Manchester City in April to keep the pressure on Premier League leaders Chelsea?

11. Chelsea pipped United to the title by a single point, but which sides finished third and fourth?

12. United benefited from 10 opposition own goals over the course of the season. Rooney and which other Red were the only two of our own players to beat that tally?

13. Injury affected the end of Rooney's campaign but how many league goals did he manage in total, on the way to winning the PFA Players' Player of the Year award?

14. Which Reds defender played in all 38 Premier League games during 2009/10?

15. Which two United midfielders made it into the PFA Team of the Year?

2010/11

1. Which English defender did United sign in July 2010?

2. In September, Dimitar Berbatov became only the fifth United player ever to do what against Liverpool?

3. Against which team did summer signing Javier Hernandez score a clever and unique backwards header?

4. In which month did Wayne Rooney ask to leave the club before signing a new five-year contract?

5. Dimitar Berbatov famously scored five goals for United against Blackburn Rovers in November 2010, helping him to win the season's Golden Boot. Who was Blackburn's goalkeeper?

6. Until what month did United remain unbeaten in the Premier League?

7. Which opponent finally defeated United to end that unbeaten run?

8. Who crossed the ball for Wayne Rooney's stunning overhead kick against Manchester City?

9. Which club legend retired in February 2011?

10. Mark Noble scored twice to put West Ham two goals ahead against United at Upton Park in April. What was the final score?

11. After how long did Javier Hernandez score in a crucial May match against Chelsea at Old Trafford?

12. Which team did United draw with to win the title, and who scored the all-important penalty?

13. Which newly promoted team did United host on the final day of the season to celebrate the title with a 4-2 win?

14. Which United player was nominated for the PFA Player of the Year and which pair were up for the Young Player of the Year?

15. Which two players announced their retirements at the end of the season, the two of them having played just under 1,000 times for United in total?

2011/12

1. Which player left Manchester United in 2011 after making 393 appearances?

2. Which player enjoyed an August testimonial against New York Cosmos?

3. Which player joined United from Atletico Madrid in the summer of 2011?

4. Who was United's club captain going into the season?

5. When Wayne Rooney scored a hat-trick – including his 150th Premier League goal – against Arsenal in an 8-2 victory, which United player scored twice?

6. Which Arsenal player was sent off that day?

7. United led the table after five wins to start the season. In what month did the Reds drop into second place?

8. Which United player scored our only goal in the 6-1 defeat to Manchester City in October 2011?

9. When United were beaten 3-2 by Blackburn Rovers on New Year's Eve, which Nigerian striker, signed from Everton the previous summer, scored twice for the visitors at Old Trafford?

10. An eight-game winning streak saw United head back to the top of the table until the end of which month?

11. How many of United's final 18 league games did Sir Alex Ferguson's side fail to win: one, two, four, or six?

12. What was the score when United visited the Etihad in April?

13. United's final Premier League game of the season was against which club?

14. How many points did both Manchester clubs finish on?

15. Wayne Rooney was the league's second top scorer – which Dutchman at a rival club won the Golden Boot with 30 goals?

2012/13

1. Manchester United began the season with an away trip to North West rivals Everton, suffering a 1-0 defeat. Which future Red scored the winner?

2. The Reds signed Arsenal forward Robin van Persie during the summer months, and he ended the season as the club's top scorer. What shirt number did he take?

3. Van Persie scored his first hat-trick for the club against which side during a superb 3-2 away win in September 2012?

4. With United eventually romping home to win the title by 11 points, who finished second behind the Reds that season?

5. Midfielder Nick Powell found the net just once during his career at Old Trafford, scoring against which side in a 4-0 home win back in September 2012?

6. Who made the most appearances for the side during the course of the season in all competitions?

7. Only two players were dismissed for the Reds during the course of the season, who were they?

8. The final day of the season marked the last day in charge of the club for Sir Alex, as the Reds played out a 5-5 draw at the Hawthorns. Which future United player scored a hat-trick against them that day?

9. And which United player scored the last goal of Sir Alex's reign in that match?

10. His final home game just seven days prior resulted in a 2-1 win over which side?

11. Who did United recruit from Crystal Palace back in January 2013, but did not make his debut until the following season?

12. Javier Hernandez wore what number for United during the duration of the season?

13. The Reds had one Danish representative during the squad that season – who was it?

14. Who scored United's decisive late winner in February 2013 at Craven Cottage, as the Reds went 13 games unbeaten in the league?

15. Stalwart defender Nemanja Vidic scored one goal all season as United romped to the title – who did his goal come against?

2013/14

1. Who finished as the club's top scorer that season with 19 goals in all competitions?

2. David Moyes was appointed as Sir Alex Ferguson's successor. Which stadium was the venue for his first United match?

3. Who did Moyes's first Premier League win as United boss come against?

4. Wayne Rooney found the net twice as United beat Aston Villa 4-1 at home in March 2014. Who scored our other two goals?

5. How many points did the Reds finish on at the end of the season – 62, 63 or 64?

6. How many clean sheets did David De Gea have at the end of the league season – 11, 12 or 13?

7. Which outfield player made the most Premier League appearances for the side that season?

8. United beat Sunderland 2-1 away in October. Which youngster scored both United goals?

9. Who scored the team's only goal in a 1-0 win over Norwich City back on 28 December 2013?

10. Chris Smalling scored his only league goal against which side in a 3-2 away win on Boxing Day?

11. Who scored the only goal of the game as United beat Arsenal 1-0 at Old Trafford?

12. Who was United's captain during the 2013/14 season?

13. Wayne Rooney famously scored from inside his own half against which London side in a 2-0 away win?

14. Ryan Giggs took over as interim boss for the final four games of the season. Who did his first victory as manager come against?

15. Which Academy striker scored twice against Hull City in our final home game of the season?

2014/15

1. This season was unusual in that the Reds didn't compete in any European competitions. In which season prior to 2014/15 did this previously occur?

2. History was made during the pre-season tour, when 109,318 supporters – a record crowd for the sport in the US – packed out Michigan Stadium to see United beat which team 3-1?

3. New manager Louis van Gaal's first home match in charge came in a high-profile pre-season friendly on 12 August 2014, with 58,381 fans in attendance at Old Trafford. Who were our Spanish opponents?

4. While Wayne Rooney took the captain's armband following the pre-season departure of Nemanja Vidic, which midfielder – who would leave for West Bromwich Albion later in the season – was named vice-captain?

5. After a strong pre-season, our Premier League campaign began with a disappointing 2-1 home defeat, against a side claiming their first-ever league win at Old Trafford. Name them.

6. There were many departures from the playing staff before the summer transfer window closed on 1 September 2014. Which Academy graduate – who moved to Arsenal for £16m – commanded the biggest fee?

7. Patrice Evra was another popular player to move on from Old Trafford in pre-season. Which club did the French full-back sign for?

8. New South American arrivals Angel Di Maria and Radamel Falcao were on target as we beat Everton 2-1 at home in October. Both would end the season with four goals apiece before departing the Reds – but which of the pair made the most appearances in all competitions?

9. Our lowest attendance of the league season – 18,098 – came in January 2015, when Marouane Fellaini and James Wilson were on target in a 2-0 league win. Name the London stadium where the game was played.

10. A young Jesse Lingard was loaned out in February 2015 – his fourth such temporary switch to a Championship side in as many seasons. Can you name all four clubs?

11. A 1-0 league win away to Newcastle in March came courtesy of an 89th-minute goal from which United wide man, following a misplaced pass from goalkeeper Tim Krul?

12. Our 2-1 league win at Anfield in March 2015 was memorable for two reasons: opposition captain Steven Gerrard being sent off 38 seconds after coming on as a half-time substitute, and which United player scoring a brilliant brace?

13. The Reds picked up a sixth straight league victory on 12 April 2015, following a thrilling win in the 169th Manchester derby. What was the full-time score at Old Trafford: 3-2, 4-2 or 5-2 to United?

14. Champions League football was secured that season, as van Gaal's Reds finished fourth. Which three other clubs also finished in the Champions League spots?

15. Which former United player was in charge of the opposition as they were relegated following a goalless draw at Old Trafford on the final day of the league season?

2015/16

1. We kicked off the campaign with a narrow 1-0 home victory against Tottenham Hotspur. Which England international full-back scored the own goal that won us the three point that day?

2. We had five debutants in that game against Spurs – an Argentinian, a Dutchman, a German, a Frenchman and an Italian. Name all five.

3. We also won our second game of the league season, Adnan Januzaj scoring in a 1-0 win at Villa Park. What was unusual about when the game was played?

4. Anthony Martial's debut goal, our third in a 3-1 win against Liverpool in September 2015, will live long in the memory. But who scored our second goal that day, from the penalty spot – his only converted spot-kick in the league as a United player?

5. Martial followed up his debut goal against Liverpool with two more in his next league appearance – a 3-2 win on the road, where United wore our black away kit. Name our opponents.

6. When Leicester's Jamie Vardy scored against United in November 2015, it was the 11th consecutive Premier League game in which he'd found the target. Which United player held the previous record of scoring in 10 consecutive games in the competition?

7. Which Watford player scored a goal for both teams – an 87th-minute penalty for the Hornets, before a decisive 90th-minute own goal as we won 2-1 in dramatic fashion at Vicarage Road in November 2015?

8. United won 1-0 at Anfield in January 2016, in what was Louis van Gaal's fourth and final league match in charge of United in a fixture against Liverpool. In how many of those four games did we emerge victorious?

9. On Valentine's weekend, which appropriately named 21-year-old defender made his first (and only) league appearance for United, after coming on as a substitute away at Sunderland?

10. Marcus Rashford had an incredible impact upon his sudden promotion to the first team in February 2016. What shirt number did Marcus wear in his first season?

11. Against which London club did Matteo Darmian score his only goal for the Reds – a 20-yarder in a 2-0 Old Trafford win in April?

12. Away from the match itself, what was significant about the Reds' league game against West Ham on 10 May 2016?

13. A final-day postponement in the Premier League led to our Old Trafford meeting with Bournemouth being rearranged. How many days later was the game eventually played?

14. And which club legend scored his 100th Premier League goal that night – our first in a 3-1 win against the Cherries?

15. Which United midfielder was the only Red to feature in all 38 of our Premier League fixtures in 2015/16?

2016/17

1. Jose Mourinho's first Premier League victory as Reds manager came on the opening day against which south-coast club?

2. On his second United debut, against Southampton, Paul Pogba started alongside which former Everton player in a two-man holding midfield?

3. Marcus Rashford's late winner at Hull was enough for victory over a Tigers side managed at the time by which former United player?

4. In September 2016, the Reds netted four first-half goals during a 4-1 home triumph against which Midlands outfit that we had also faced in the Community Shield at the start of the season.

5. In our 3-1 win over Swansea at the Liberty Stadium in November 2016, Zlatan Ibrahimovic scored the Premier League's 25,000th goal, but did he bring the milestone up with his first or second strike of the day?

6. An inspired goalkeeping performance from which Reds Academy graduate saw United held to a 0-0 draw by a visiting Burnley side in October 2016?

7. Zlatan Ibrahimovic was named the Premier League's Player of the Month for December 2016, becoming the first United player to win the award since September 2015. Which Red won the award on that occasion?

8. Henrikh Mkhitaryan's famous scorpion-kick goal on Boxing Day came against which club?

9. Who got the goals in a 2-0 win over West Ham on our first-ever trip to the London Stadium?

10. Wayne Rooney became our all-time leading goalscorer with a stoppage-time equaliser at Stoke, scored in which minute?

11. We became the first club to reach 600 all-time Premier League wins with a 3-1 victory over which team, in March 2017?

12. Between defeats in the capital at Chelsea (October 2016) and Arsenal (May 2017), the Reds went on an unbeaten streak in the league lasting how many matches?

13. Jose Mourinho handed first-team debuts to four young Reds in a final-day clash with Crystal Palace. Can you name the quartet?

14. United lost just once in the Premier League at Old Trafford in the 2016/17 campaign, to which team?

15. Zlatan Ibrahimovic topped United's scoring charts in the competition, in his first Premier League season, with how many goals?

2017/18

1. Who was United's first senior signing of the summer transfer window, joining from Portuguese club Benfica?

2. We won our opening two games of the league season – against West Ham and Swansea City – by the same scoreline. What was it?

3. Zlatan Ibrahimovic rejoined the club in August 2017, opting for which shirt number upon his return?

4. Which Red won the Premier League's Goal of the Month award for September 2017 with a ferocious strike against Everton?

5. In our first eight Premier League matches, we kept seven clean sheets. Who were the only team to find the net against us during that run?

6. Who netted a brace for the Reds in our 4-2 win at his old club Watford in November 2017?

7. On New Year's Day of 2018, United won 2-0 at the home of which Merseyside club?

8. In January, Alexis Sanchez made the move to Old Trafford from Arsenal. He had already played against United in the league earlier in the season, true or false?

9. Which stadium was our January away trip to Tottenham Hotspur played at, while they awaited the building of their new ground?

10. Nemanja Matic scored a late winner to see the Reds come from 2-0 down to beat Crystal Palace 3-2 at Selhurst Park, but which two players had already got on the scoresheet for United earlier that evening?

11. Who provided the assists for both the equaliser and the eventual winner in our 3-2 comeback victory away to Manchester City?

12. Michael Carrick made his 464th and last appearance for the club on the final day of the season, captaining the Reds against which side?

13. David De Gea topped our 2017/18 appearance chart in the competition with how many games played?

14. United's English players accounted for 21 of our 68 league goals in the campaign, with our Belgian contingents' combined total just one less. Which nation's Reds accounted for the third-highest number with 15?

15. United faced two opponents in the Premier League for the first time over the course of the season. Who were they?

2018/19

1. Who was United's club captain in the 2018/19 season?

2. Which defender returned to his boyhood club in the summer?

3. Which player did we sign from Porto at the start of the season?

4. United kicked off the season with a 2-1 win at home to Leicester City. Which player scored his first career goal in that victory?

5. And which midfielder made his debut in that match?

6. The last match of Jose Mourinho's United reign was against which team?

7. And Ole Gunnar Solskjaer's first match as caretaker manager was away to which team?

8. What was the score in that match?

9. Who scored the first goal of Solskjaer's spell in charge?

10. Who scored his first goal for United with a dramatic injury-time equaliser at home to Burnley in January?

11. What was the score when United took on Tottenham at their temporary home in January's league meeting?

12. Marouane Fellaini left the club in the winter transfer window. Which country was his next destination?

13. Which young Academy graduate midfielder made his senior United debut as a late substitute in February's 3-1 win away to Crystal Palace?

14. Another Academy graduate's superb strike against Southampton in March was later voted United's Goal of the Season. Who scored it?

15. Which midfielder was United's top scorer for the season in all competitions, with 16 goals?

2019/20

1. Who was named United club captain at the start of the season following the departure of Antonio Valencia?

2. Who did United beat 4-0 on the opening weekend of the Premier League season?

3. And which player scored on his United debut that day?

4. United's 2,000th Premier League goal was scored in an away game with Norwich in October. Which Academy graduate scored that landmark goal?

5. Which former United Academy player scored against his former club for Bournemouth in November?

6. The Reds won the first Manchester derby of the season 2-1 at the Etihad Stadium in December. Who were the United goalscorers?

7. Which Manchester United player signed for Internazionale in January 2020?

8. Name the striker we brought in on loan in that January transfer window.

9. Which side did we buy Bruno Fernandes from in the January transfer window?

10. And against which club did he make his United debut?

11. Bruno provided an assist in his first away game for United against Chelsea – for which player?

12. Scott McTominay famously scored our last goal in front of fans for a long time in the Manchester derby at Old Trafford in March 2020. Who got the other goal in that 2-0 win?

13. Who were the opposition in our first behind-closed-doors league game following the resumption of league action in June?

14. Who scored our last goal of the Premier League season to secure our Champions League qualification?

15. And against which team was that win secured?

2020/21

1. Due to the pandemic, United were only able to play one pre-season friendly. Against which Premier League club was this match played?

2. Which player scored on his United debut in our Premier League opener against Crystal Palace?

3. And which former United player scored twice in that game?

4. There were three new recruits on transfer deadline day in October – Edinson Cavani, Facundo Pellistri and which other player?

5. What was remarkable about United's first winning goal in the '20/21 Premier League campaign?

6. Harry Maguire scored his first goal of the season in the 4-1 away win against which Premier League team?

7. What was the score in our first league meeting with Leeds in December 2020?

8. Who were on the wrong end of an unfortunate 9-0 beating in February 2021?

9. One of those goals was an own goal, but how many of the United goalscorers can you name?

10. Name the Newcastle-born Academy graduate who made his United debut against his hometown club in February 2021.

11. Bruno Fernandes and which other player scored in our 2-0 win away to Manchester City in March 2021?

12. Bruno's penalty in that match made him third on the list of all-time penalty scorers for United. Which two players were ahead of him in that list?

13. Who provided the opposition for Old Trafford's first match in front of fans for over a year?

14. And how many fans were allowed into the stadium?

15. Who scored more goals for United in all competitions 2020/21, Marcus Rashford or Edinson Cavani?

2021/22

1. United kicked off the Premier League season with a 5-1 win over which historic rivals?

2. And who scored his first United hat-trick in that win?

3. The Reds' three big signings were Cristiano Ronaldo, Jadon Sancho and which other player?

4. United won 3-0 in London on 30 October. Against which team was that?

5. Jadon Sancho scored his first Premier League goal against which team?

6. Michael Carrick had three matches as caretaker manager. Against which club was his final game in charge, a 3-2 win at Old Trafford?

7. Which player scored the first goal of Ralf Rangnick's time in charge, in a 1-0 win over Crystal Palace?

8. In December United had two Premier League games postponed due to Covid outbreaks. Who were the opposition for those matches (*Clue: both team names begin with the same letter*)?

9. Which promoted side were downed 1-0 by a Cristiano Ronaldo penalty in December?

10. We played the same team twice in consecutive matches in January, first at home in the Cup and then away in the League. Who was the opposition?

11. This was the second time this had happened in 2021/22. Which team did we face in consecutive matches in September, in the League and the League Cup?

12. Which Academy graduate opened the scoring in United's 3-1 win away to Brentford in January?

13. David De Gea kept his 162nd clean sheet for United in the 1-0 win over West Ham in January. Which Cup-winning 'keeper did he pass on the all-time list of clean sheets for the club?

14. Which defender opened the scoring for the Reds in our 4-2 win away to Leeds in February?

15. Who did Cristiano Ronaldo score the second hat-trick of his United career against in March?

FA CUP

How have the Reds fared in the world's oldest national football competition?

MANCHESTER UNITED F.C. LTD.
F.A. CUP 5th ROUND
MANCHESTER UNITED v. SHEFFIELD WEDNESDAY
AT OLD TRAFFORD
KICK-OFF 3 p.m.
SATURDAY, 15th FEBRUARY, 1958
GROUNDSIDE
Admission 2/-
It is recommended that this ticket be presented at least 30 minutes before Kick-Off
Issued subject to the Rules, Regulations and Bye-Laws of the Football Association.
NO MONEY RETURNED.
TO BE GIVEN UP

1. In which decade was United's first-ever FA Cup game?

2. Who was the first Red to score an FA Cup goal at the new Wembley Stadium (after it was reopened in 2007)?

3. Which Midlands club have United faced most often in the FA Cup without ever having faced the same side in a top-flight league fixture?

4. Which Reds legend once scored six goals in an FA Cup game, away to Northampton Town in February 1970?

5. Which player has lifted the FA Cup on the most occasions as United captain, doing so three times?

6. And, other than him, who is the only player to lift the Cup as Reds skipper more than once?

7. Which stadium has hosted the most of United's FA Cup away games – seven times as of the end of the 2021/22 season?

8. And who are the Reds most frequent Cup opponents at Old Trafford across the same period, with nine meetings?

9. Up to and including the 2021/22 season, who were the last club United faced in the FA Cup for the first time in the competition?

10. Name the first Reds debutant of the 21st century whose first United game featured him scoring a goal in the FA Cup.

11. Who was United's top scorer in Cup fixtures played at the Millennium Stadium in Cardiff, with four goals in three appearances?

12. At the conclusion of 2021/22, which Midlands side had United beaten more times than any other club in the FA Cup, with 11 victories from 13 meetings?

13. Against which club did United triumph in the short-lived FA Cup third-fourth place match in 1970?

14. Paul Scholes's 'second debut' for the Reds was in an FA Cup meeting with which side?

15. Which prolific forward holds the record for most goals by a United player in a single campaign, netting 10 in 1963/64?

16. Back in the days of multiple replays, how many times did the Reds and Birmingham, then known as Small Heath, face each other in the Cup in 1903/04 before the intermediate round tie was settled – a record such number for United?

17. Which of the teams competing in the 2021/22 Premier League had, as of the end of that season, gone the longest without facing United in the FA Cup?

18. Who scored United's first home FA Cup goal of the 21st century, against Portsmouth in January 2003?

19. In which round have United been eliminated in the FA Cup most often – third, fourth or fifth?

20. Which member of United's 2021/22 squad had scored the most overall FA Cup goals as of the end of that season?

21. Who was the most recent player to score their first FA Cup goal for United?

22. What was the score when United beat Yeovil in 1949 for the club's biggest-ever FA Cup victory?

23. Which team were both United's last FA Cup opponents of 2018/19, and the first of the following season?

24. With 78 appearances, who is, as of the end of 2021/22, the Reds' record appearance-maker in the FA Cup?

25. How many victories did United claim in the club's longest FA Cup winning streak, between March 1963 and February 1964 – eight, nine or 10?

26. In which year was the first FA Cup tie at Old Trafford?

27. Who were Sir Alex Ferguson's first FA Cup opponents?

28. And who were Sir Alex Ferguson's last FA Cup opponents?

29. As of the end of 2021/22, in which year did United last fail to score in a home FA Cup fixture – 2010, 2015 or 2020?

30. How many of United's 30 appearances in the Charity/Community Shield came solely as a result of winning the FA Cup, as of the end of 2021/22?

31. Which 2021/22 top-flight club have United faced the most times in the FA Cup while winning every meeting (four), with four victories from four games as of the end of that season?

32. And as of the same date, against which club have United hit the most FA Cup goals, with 32 strikes in 15 games – Reading, Everton or Blackburn Rovers?

33. Against which club did Matt Busby oversee his first FA Cup tie as Manchester United manager, in January 1946?

34. Up until May 2022, who had scored United's most recent FA Cup hat-trick, hitting a treble against West Ham in 1985?

35. Which prolific forward and United Academy product made his final Reds appearance in the 1995 FA Cup final?

36. In which decade did United reach the most of the club's FA Cup finals?

37. Of the players to start either leg of the 1992 FA Youth Cup final, who went on to win the FA Cup the most times with the United senior side?

38. Who, as of 2022, are the only side to have lifted the FA Cup on more occasions than the Reds?

39. United's first FA Cup penalty shoot-out came in 1992 – who were the opponents?

40. Name either of the United players to score in that shoot-out?

41. Which Arsenal player had a penalty saved in United's epic FA Cup semi-final replay triumph in 1999?

42. And which opposition player was denied by David De Gea when the Reds faced Everton in the last four in 2016?

43. After Wembley, at which venue have most of United's neutral FA Cup fixtures been played, to the end of 2022?

44. In which decade did United reach 100 FA Cup goals – 1900s, 1930s or 1950s?

45. How many matches did the Reds play in our 2005 FA Cup run, ultimately finishing as losing finalists?

46. Which outfield player went in goal in the 2008 FA Cup quarter-final against Portsmouth, after Edwin van der Sar picked up an injury and his half-time replacement Tomasz Kuszczak was sent off?

47. How many goals did the Reds score during the Cup runs of 1896/97 and 1948/49, a joint-club record for most strikes in a single FA Cup campaign – 13, 23 or 33?

48. Which frontman has the best FA Cup goals-to-games ratio among those to net at least 10 times for the Reds in the competition, doing so at a rate of one per game with 14 strikes in 14 appearances?

49. Which player has made the most FA Cup appearances for United of those representing a nation outside of the British Isles – Peter Schmeichel, Jaap Stam or Eric Cantona?

50. Who were the Reds' opponents in the 2015/16 quarter-finals – the last-ever last-eight fixture to go to a replay?

51. Who are the two clubs to have both won and lost against United in an FA Cup final, as of the end of 2021/22?

52. Which former United defender was part of the Leicester City side that lifted the FA Cup in 2021?

53. How many FA Cup final appearances did United make at the Millennium Stadium in Cardiff?

54. Which Yorkshire club were the first team to lift the FA Cup at Old Trafford, in a replay in 1911 – Leeds or Bradford City?

55. Which three Welsh sides have United played in the FA Cup?

56. Against which Somerset club have United played the most FA Cup games (four) without ever conceding a goal?

57. Which club have United faced most often during Cup-winning campaigns, having met them en route to lifting the trophy five times up until the end of 2021/22?

58. Which club's only FA Cup meeting with United up until the end of 2021/22 came in a final?

59. Which other 'United' have the Reds faced most often in the FA Cup up until the end of the 2021/22 campaign?

60. Which London club have United faced in Cup replays in the most different seasons, doing so in five separate campaigns?

61. Which North East side did the Reds face in an FA Cup replay in 1970, 1971 and 1972?

62. In which year did we face QPR in our last-ever second replay?

63. United played 14 FA Cup ties at Maine Road, but how many of those were semi-final ties – four, five or six?

64. How many clean sheets did Sergio Romero keep in his 17 FA Cup appearances for United – three, 13 or 17?

65. Up until the end of 2021/22, who was the last former United player to net against the Reds in the FA Cup?

66. In how many consecutive FA Cup games did the Reds find the net between January 1977 and January 1980, for a club-record scoring streak in the competition – 11, 21 or 31?

67. Which trophy have United won outright more often – the FA Cup or the Charity/Community Shield?

68. How many times have we won a league and FA Cup double?

69. And in which year did the Reds first do so?

70. Six players shared the United record for most successfully converted FA Cup penalties, excluding shoot-outs, as of the end of 2021/22. How many had each scored – three or four?

71. What is the greatest number of games United can currently play in an FA Cup season, excluding replays?

72. What was the score when United beat Brentford in January 1928 for the club's biggest FA Cup win to date at Old Trafford?

73. What is the biggest gap, in years, between FA Cup final appearances for United?

74. And what is United's record for most consecutive FA Cup finals reached?

75. What is the Reds' joint-biggest victory in an FA Cup semi-final, having been achieved previously against Oldham, Newcastle and Watford?

76. Which defender made the most FA Cup appearances for United without ever scoring in the competition, playing 60 times in total?

77. Other than Cristiano Ronaldo, which member of the Reds' 2021/22 squad was the first to make an FA Cup appearance for United?

78. Which club have the Reds faced most often in the FA Cup without the two sides ever having met in a final?

79. Who scored the winning goal in United's first FA Cup tie played behind closed doors, during the 2020 summer lockdown period?

80. How many different players found the net when United beat Tranmere 6-0 in January 2020 – an FA Cup record for the Reds?

81. And how many of those players netted their first Reds goal in the process?

82. Who started for United against his former club in the 2018 FA Cup final?

83. And which player was also in the starting XI for that final having found the net in the previous year's final for a different club?

84. How many of United's seven FA Cup meetings with Liverpool at home, as of the end of 2021/22, have ended in home victories?

85. Who scored the only goal of the game in a 1-0 FA Cup third-round win for the Reds in January 2021, then repeated the feat at the same stage a year later?

86. Who is the most successful player in FA Cup history to have lifted the trophy with United and another club?

87. What number ball were United in the 2021/22 FA Cup third-round draw? *(Clue: it's Dean Henderson's squad number in the 2021/22 season).*

88. What is the latest month of a year in which United have played an FA Cup fixture, albeit not having done so since 1903?

89. Ryan Giggs famously scored United's FA Cup winner against Arsenal in the 1999 semi-final replay, but who got the Reds' other goal that evening?

90. Which future United striker scored for Liverpool at Old Trafford in the FA Cup in 1999, before two late goals gave Alex Ferguson's side victory?

91. Who scored in both United's final FA Cup game of the 20th century and the Reds' first outing in the competition during the 21st century?

92. Who hit the most FA Cup goals for United during Sir Alex Ferguson's reign as manager, with 17?

93. And who were the Reds' first FA Cup opponents away from home under the leadership of the legendary Scot?

94. Up until the end of 2021/22, in which year were United last defeated in an FA Cup replay?

95. United's last FA Cup tie before the Second World War was against which Midlands club?

96. Which goalkeeper has made the most FA Cup appearances for United as of the end of 2021/22?

97. What is the greatest number of FA Cup games the Reds have played in a single season, doing so in both 1969/70 and 1978/79?

98. Which manager has been in charge both for and against United in the FA Cup at Wembley?

99. Who were United's first FA Cup opponents at Wembley in a game that was not a final?

100. Who were the Reds' most recent non-league opponents in the FA Cup, as of the end of 2021/22?

WINNING FA CUP FINALS

Twelve trophy-lifting occasions to reflect on, beginning in 1909

THE 1909 FA CUP FINAL

1. Fill in the missing details in the match – opponent and the United goalscorer.

Manchester United 1 __________ 0

(________ 22 mins)

2. Fill in the missing players in the starting XI…

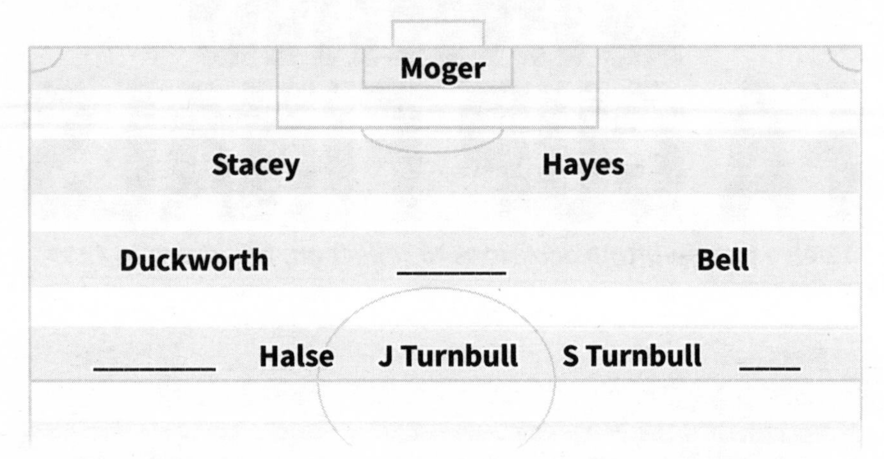

3. Who was the United manager for our first FA Cup triumph?

4. Who was the captain who lifted the trophy

5. What was the venue for the final?

THE 1948 FA CUP FINAL

1. Fill in the missing details in the match – opponent and the United goalscorers.

Manchester United 4 __________ 2

(________ 28, 70 mins, _________ 80 mins, _________ 82 mins)

2. Fill in the missing players in the starting XI…

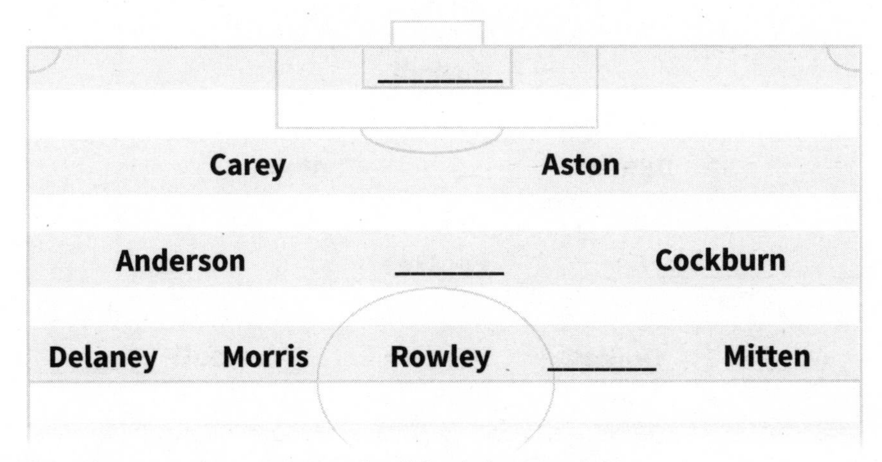

3. Who was the captain who lifted the trophy?

4. Which all-time England legend was on the losing side?

5. What colour shirts did United wear in the match?

THE 1963 FA CUP FINAL

1. Fill in the missing details in the match – opponent and the United goalscorers.

   Manchester United 3 __________ 1

   (________ 30 mins, ________ 56, 85 mins)

2. Fill in the missing players in the starting XI…

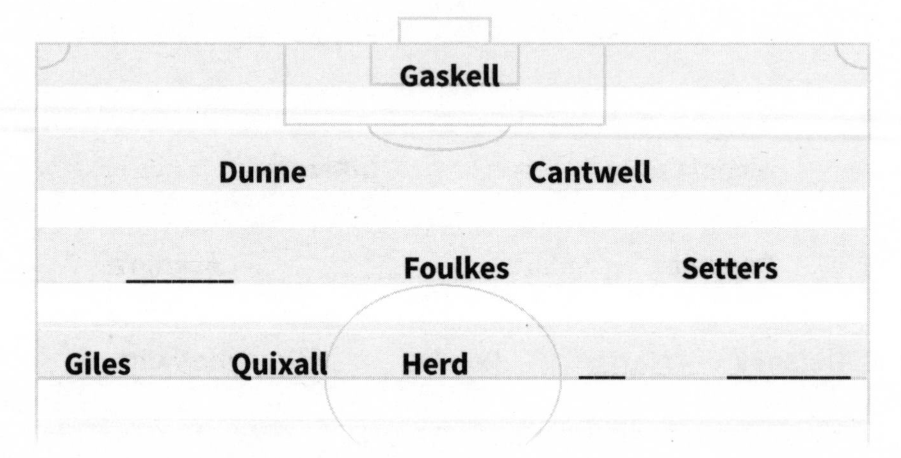

3. Who was the captain who lifted the trophy?

4. Which legendary goalkeeper was in nets for the opposition?

5. What nationality were both the United goalscorers?

THE 1977 FA CUP FINAL

1. Fill in the missing details in the match – opponent and the United goalscorers.

Manchester United 2 __________ 1

(________ 50 mins, ________ 55 mins)

2. Fill in the missing players in the starting XI…

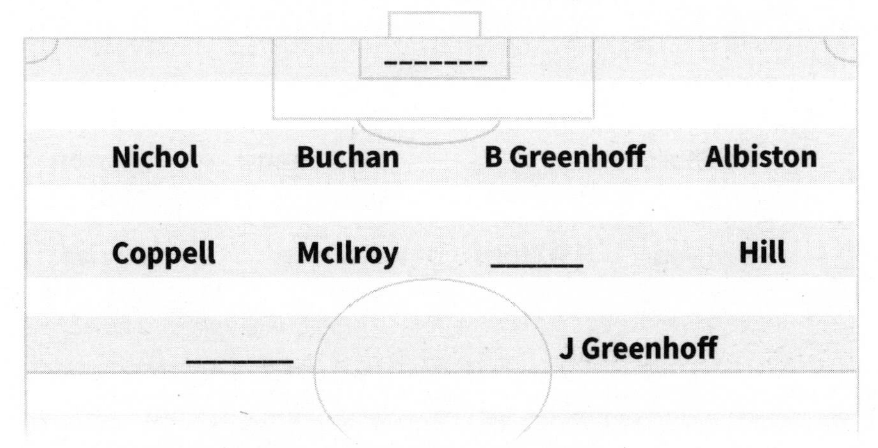

3. Who was the captain who lifted the trophy?

4. Who scored the goal for the opposition?

5. Which of the Greenhoff brothers was the older?

THE 1983 FA CUP FINAL REPLAY

1. Fill in the missing details in the match – opponent and the United goalscorers.

   Manchester United 4 __________ 0

   (________ 25, 44 mins, ________ 30 mins, ________ 62 mins)

2. Fill in the missing players in the starting XI…

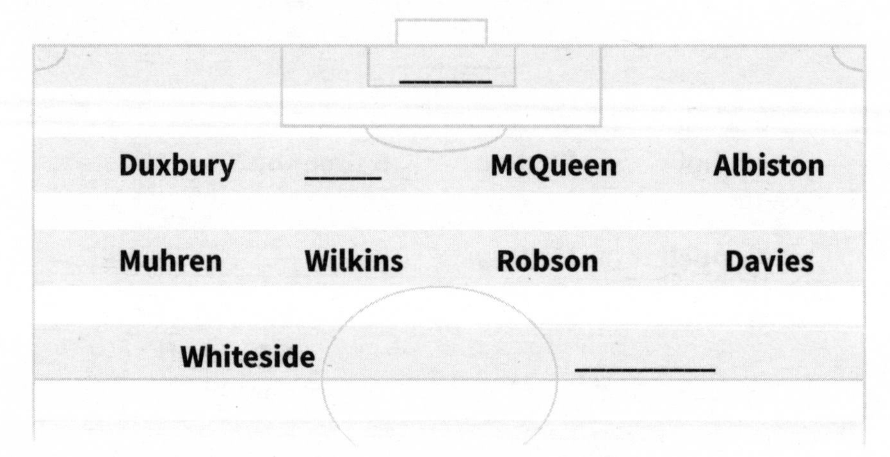

3. Who was the captain who lifted the trophy?

4. What was the score in the first final?

5. On which day of the week was this Cup final replay played?

THE 1985 FA CUP FINAL

1. Fill in the missing details in the match – opponent and the United goalscorers.

   Manchester United 1 __________ 0

   (________ 110 mins)

2. Fill in the missing players in the starting XI...

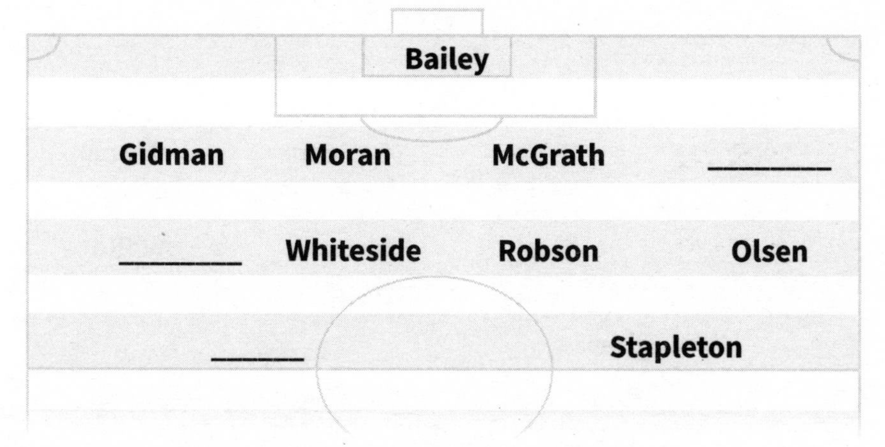

3. Who was the captain who lifted the trophy?

4. Kevin Moran famously received the FA Cup final's first red card for a tackle on which opposition player?

5. And what was the name of the referee who sent him off?

THE 1990 FA CUP FINAL REPLAY

1. Fill in the missing details in the match – opponent and the United goalscorers.

Manchester United 1 __________ 0

(________ 59 mins)

2. Fill in the missing players in the starting XI…

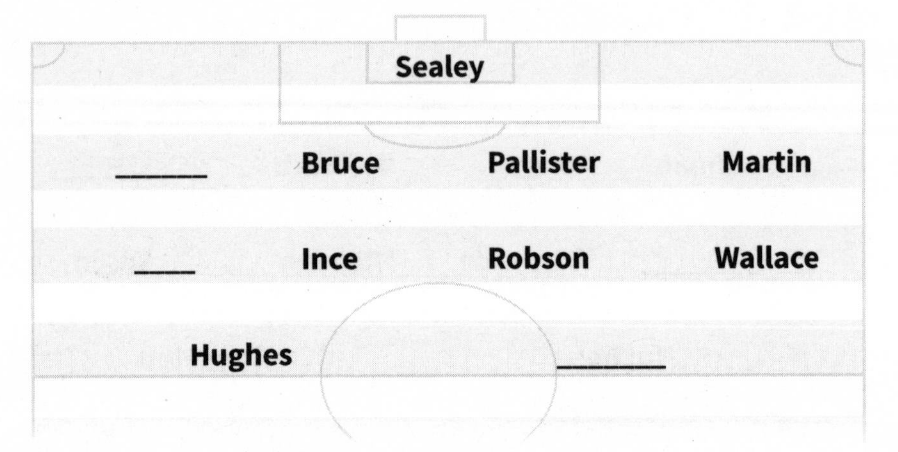

3. Who was the captain who lifted the trophy?

4. Who was in goal for United in the first match?

5. Which former United star managed the opposition?

THE 1994 FA CUP FINAL

1. Fill in the missing details in the match – opponent and the United goalscorers.

   Manchester United 4 __________ 0

   (________ 60, 66 mins; __________ 69 mins, ________ 90 mins)

2. Fill in the missing players in the starting XI…

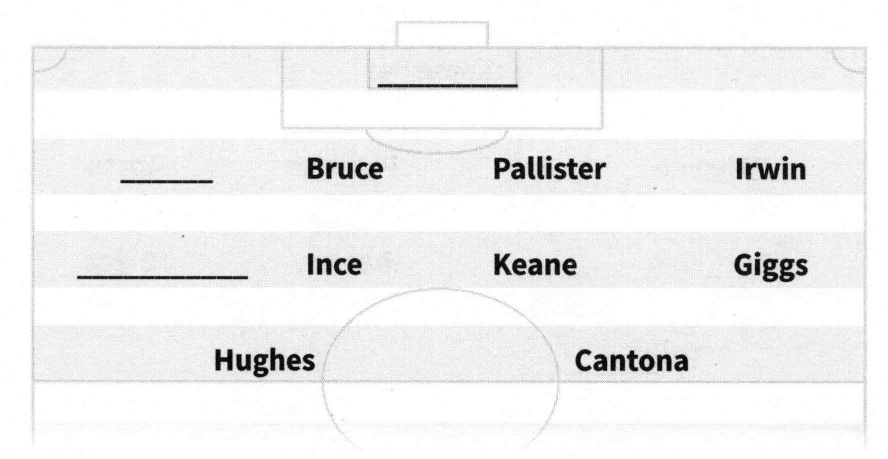

3. Who was the captain who lifted the trophy?

4. Which one of the goalscorers came off the bench?

5. Who was the manager of the opposition?

THE 1996 FA CUP FINAL

1. Fill in the missing details in the match – opponent and the United goalscorers.

   Manchester United 1 __________ 0

   (________ 85 mins)

2. Fill in the missing players in the starting XI…

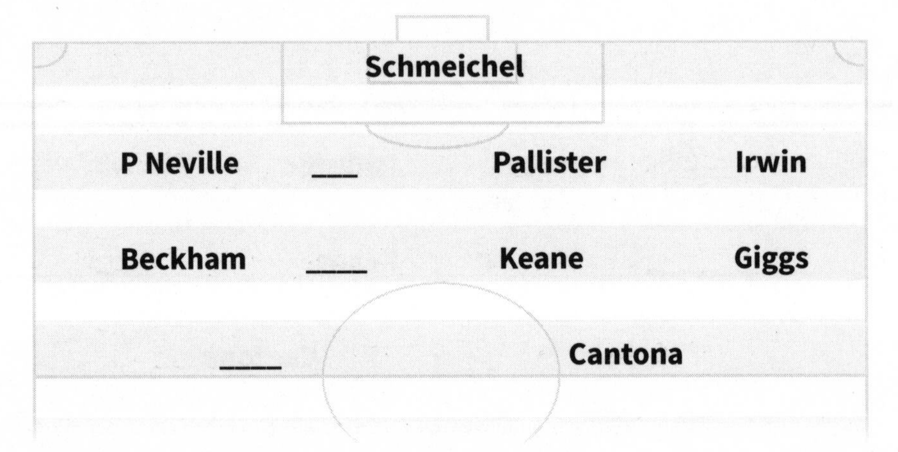

3. Who was the captain who lifted the trophy?

4. Which two Class of '92 players came off the bench in this final?

5. What colour shirts were the opposition wearing in this final?

THE 1999 FA CUP FINAL

1. Fill in the missing details in the match – opponent and the United goalscorers.

   Manchester United 2 __________ 0
   (________ 11 mins, ________ 53 mins)

2. Fill in the missing players in the starting XI…

	Schmeichel		
G Neville	May	_______	P Neville
_______	Scholes	Keane	Giggs
Cole		__________	

3. Who was the captain who lifted the trophy?

4. Which United played went off injured after just nine minutes?

5. Who was named Man of the Match?

THE 2004 FA CUP FINAL

1. Fill in the missing details in the match – opponent and the United goalscorers.

Manchester United 3 __________ 0

(________ 44 mins, ________ 65 mins, 81 mins)

2. Fill in the missing players in the starting XI…

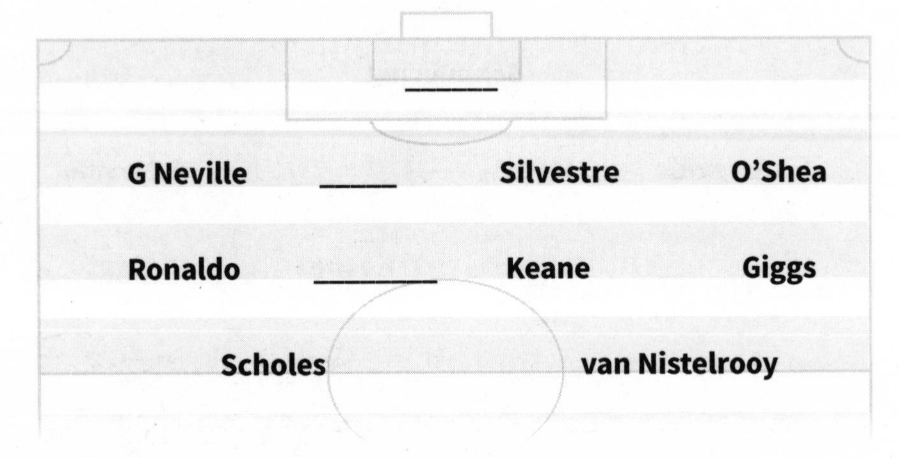

3. Who was the captain who lifted the trophy?

4. Unusually, a goalkeeper came on as a sub for United. Name him.

5. Who was the Millwall player-manager who had previously faced United in an FA Cup final?

THE 2016 FA CUP FINAL

1. Fill in the missing details in the match – opponent and the United goalscorers.

   Manchester United 2 __________ 1 (aet)

   (________ 81 mins, ________ 110 mins)

2. Fill in the missing players in the starting XI…

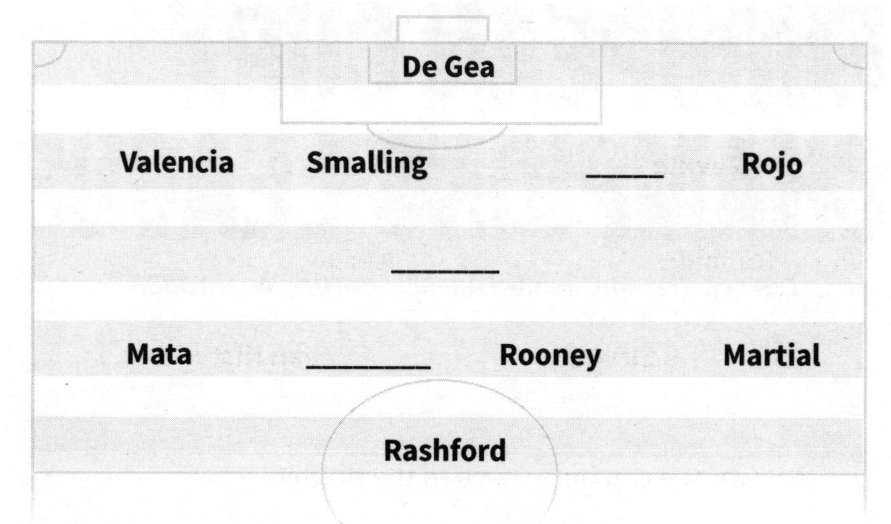

3. Who was the captain who lifted the trophy?

4. Which United player was sent off during extra-time?

5. What was the name of the former United player in the opposition starting XI

EUROPEAN CUP / CHAMPIONS LEAGUE

Our top-tier continental quests, starting out in 1956

1. In which country was the first leg of United's first-ever European Cup tie?

2. What was the aggregate score of that tie?

3. The Reds' first run in the competition ended at the semi-final stage with defeat to which team?

4. In their final match together before the Munich Air Disaster, the Busby Babes fought out a 3-3 draw – and 5-4 aggregate win – against which opponents?

5. Later that season, who scored the late penalty to secure an unlikely semi-final first leg win over AC Milan?

6. United next competed in the European Cup in 1964/65, starting in which country?

7. In that term's quarter-finals, George Best led a demolition of Benfica – what score did United famously win by in the second leg in Portugal?

8. In the 1967/68 campaign, United played away ties in four countries – fill in the missing country: Malta, Yugoslavia, ______, Spain

9. The Reds famously reached their first final in 1968 after a thrilling 3-3 semi-final, second leg draw at Real Madrid, but which player scored the first leg winner at Old Trafford?

10. Against which team did United begin their defence of the European Cup in 1968/69?

11. That defence ended at the semi-final stage after a 1-2 aggregate defeat to which *Serie A* side?

12. Over 24 years passed before the Reds returned to the competition, beating Kispest Honved 3-2 in September 1993 – which recent signing scored twice that night?

13. United's return to the competition was short-lived, following an away-goals defeat to Galatasaray after a goalless draw in which stadium?

14. In 1994/95, the Reds appeared in the new-look Champions League group stage for the first time. Which three other teams made up the group?

15. Which future United player scored against the Reds on matchday five that season?

16. The 1996/97 group stage began with a 0-1 defeat to a Juventus team managed by whom?

17. A first-ever group-stage away win was secured against which Turkish opponents?

18. How did those same opponents make history in the return encounter?

19. The Reds' maiden group-stage qualification was secured by a matchday six away win over which side?

20. Porto were steamrollered 4-0 in that season's quarter-final, first-leg encounter – which unlikely player opened the scoring that night?

21. Both legs of the '96/97 semi-final against Borussia Dortmund finished with the same scoreline – what was that?

22. In 1997/98, how many of the 18 available group-stage points did United take?

23. United were enraged by a challenge from Paul Bosvelt during a 3-1 win over Feyenoord – which Premier League team did the Dutchman later join?

24. Who scored his first European hat-trick for United that night?

25. Which future Red kept goal for Monaco in both legs of their shock quarter-final win over the Reds?

26. In 1998/99's thrilling group stage, how many goals did United score in total?

27. Which United forward netted two headers in the Reds' quarter-final, first-leg win over Inter?

28. Which future Premier League manager opened the scoring for Juventus at Old Trafford in the semi-final, first leg?

29. Two players got both a goal and an assist in the unforgettable semi-final success at the Stadio Delle Alpi – name them.

30. The Reds' 1999/2000 Champions League defence began with a dour goalless draw against a Croatia Zagreb team managed by which famous Argentina international?

31. United's group-stage win over Sturm Graz took place in a venue named after which Hollywood star?

32. UEFA trialled the second group-stage for the first time in 99/00 – which three teams were United paired with in the latter group?

33. Andy Cole's hat-trick against Anderlecht to open the 2000/01 campaign moved him to the top of the Reds' European Cup scoring charts, moving which club legend into second spot?

34. Which German side knocked United out of the 2000/01 quarter-finals after winning both legs?

35. In 2001/02, what shock world event caused the postponement of United's matchday two meeting with Olympiacos in Greece?

36. Deportivo la Coruna beat United home and away in the group stage, while the Reds returned the favour in the quarter-finals – what was the total scoreline over the four games?

37. United exited at the semi-final stage, missing out on the final which was hosted in which British city?

38. After finishing third in the 2001/02 Premier League, the Reds had to navigate a 2002/03 qualifying tie against which Hungarian side?

39. Which player scored his long-awaited first goal for the club with a penalty against Maccabi Haifa?

40. Who scored home and away against Juventus in that season's second group stage?

41. How many clean sheets did United keep in the 2003/04 group stage?

42. Which future Middlesbrough striker scored home and away for Fenerbahce against the Reds in 2004/05?

43. In November 2004, which player scored the opening goal as Lyon were beaten in Sir Alex Ferguson's 1,000th match as United manager?

44. Which former Reds defender was among AC Milan's players as United exited from the second round?

45. United met Villarreal for the first time in September 2005, with the final score also being replicated in the sides' next three Champions League encounters. What score did they all finish?

46. Which side did the Reds face on matchday six in both 2005/06 and 2006/07 group stages?

47. Which on-loan forward scored his first and only Champions League goal for the Reds to sink Lille at Old Trafford?

48. Who managed Roma during the Reds' 8-3 aggregate quarter-final win?

49. Which United player opened the 2007/08 group-stage campaign by scoring a diving header against his former team?

50. The Reds posted a club-record points haul in the 2007/08 group stage – did they amass 15, 16 or 18 points in total?

51. Across six knockout legs against Lyon, Roma and Barcelona, the Reds recorded five clean sheets, conceding just one goal. Which player scored it?

52. Which recent signing netted twice in his first European outing, 2008's group-stage win at Aalborg?

53. United progressed from the 2008/09 group stage unbeaten, but having won how many games?

54. Which future Reds boss was in charge of Internazionale during the sides' 2009 second-round encounter?

55. The 3-1 semi-final, second leg obliteration of Arsenal is part of club folklore, but who scored the only goal of the Reds' 1-0 triumph at Old Trafford?

56. On matchday six in the 2009/10 group stage, which two midfielders deputised in defence for the injury-hit Reds at Wolfsburg?

57. What was the aggregate score as AC Milan were ousted in that season's second round?

58. Who opened the scoring at Old Trafford as the Reds exited on away goals to Bayern Munich?

59. In the 2010/11 second-round tie with Marseille, which former United defender lined up for the *Ligue 1* side?

60. In that season's semi-finals, United overpowered a Schalke team managed by who?

61. What was remarkable about Wayne Rooney's brace against Otelul Galati in 2011/12?

62. United exited that term's group stage, losing how many games?

63. In 2012/13, United qualified from the group stage with how many games to spare?

64. Sir Alex Ferguson's final Champions League tie in charge ended with a 1-2 home defeat to Real Madrid – who scored the Reds' goal that evening?

65. True or false: United's biggest Champions League group-stage away win was secured under David Moyes's management.

66. Which player hit his third United hat-trick to overturn a two-goal first-leg defeat to Olympiacos in the 2013/14 second round?

67. Wayne Rooney hit the eighth and final hat-trick of his Reds career against which team in the 2015/16 qualifying rounds?

68. How did United qualify for the 2017/18 Champions League?

69. Which local lad netted on his first Champions League outing in that season's 3-0 group-stage win over Basel?

70. Which *La Liga* side ended the Reds' involvement in the 2017/18 competition?

71. A thrilling late 2018/19 group-stage win in Turin against Juventus was sparked by which player's sublime free-kick?

72. What was historically significant about United's 3-1 second-round win over PSG that term?

73. Which Reds forward hit the winner when the Reds overcame PSG in Paris in the 2020/21 group stage?

74. What was historically significant about United's dramatic 2-1 win over Villarreal in the 2021/22 group stage?

75. Who netted his first goal for the club during the Reds' 2-0 win at Villarreal later that term?

WINNING EUROPEAN CUP/ CHAMPIONS LEAGUE FINALS

Three euphoric European nights to challenge yourselves on

THE 1968 EUROPEAN CUP FINAL

1. Fill in the missing details in the match – opponent and the United goalscorers.

   Manchester United 4 __________ 1

   (________ 53, 99 mins, ________ 93 mins, _______ 94 mins)

2. Fill in the missing players in the starting XI…

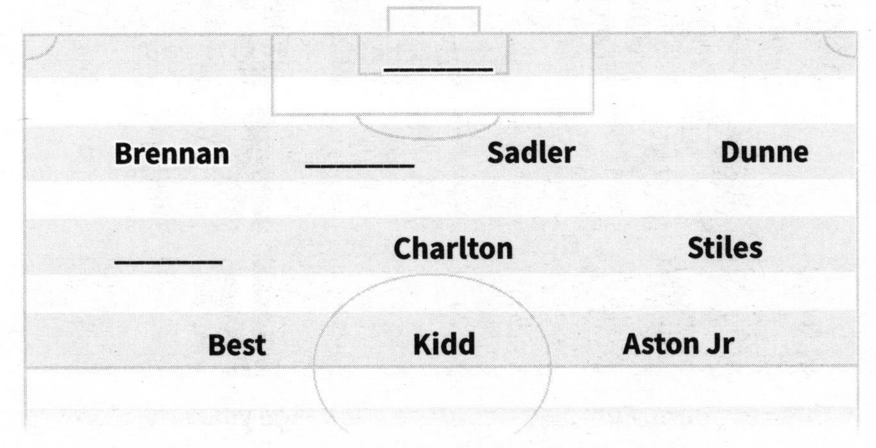

3. Who was the United captain who lifted the trophy?

4. What was the venue for the final?

5. Which United player celebrated his 19th birthday on this day?

THE 1999 CHAMPIONS LEAGUE FINAL

1. Fill in the missing details in the match – opponent and the United goalscorers.

   Manchester United 2 __________ 1

   (________ 91 mins, _________ 93 mins)

2. Fill in the missing players in the starting XI...

		Schmeichel	
G Neville	**Stam**	**_______**	**Irwin**
Giggs	**Butt**	**Beckham**	**_________**
____		**Yorke**	

3. Who was the United captain who lifted the trophy?

4. Which two players made way for the two matchwinning substitutes?

5. Who scored the opening goal for the opposition?

THE 2008 CHAMPIONS LEAGUE FINAL

1. Fill in the missing details in the match – opponent and the United goalscorers.

Manchester United 1 __________ 1

(________ 26 mins)

2. Fill in the missing players in the starting XI…

3. Which two United players lifted the trophy together?

4. Who scored the opposition's equalising goal?

5. Name the six players who scored United's penalties in the shoot-out.

OTHER EUROPEAN COMPETITIONS

More campaigns on the continent, including the UEFA Cup and Cup Winners' Cup

1. In which season did United first take part in a European competition that wasn't the European Cup?

2. Which English team did United beat 4-3 on aggregate in the second round of that tournament?

3. Name the four other British sides that United have faced in European competitions other than the European Cup/ Champions League.

4. What was the official name of the European competition that United first competed in during the 1964/65 season?

5. And how did United qualify for that competition?

6. United beat a German team 10-1 on aggregate in the second round of that competition – who was it?

7. The Reds made it through to semi-final of that tournament in 1964/65, losing to Hungarian side Ferencvaros. In which month of the year was that semi-final second leg played?

8. The first team we played in the renamed UEFA Cup, in 1976, was a famous European name hugely successful in the 1970s – who were they?

9. We were knocked out of that tournament in the second round, against another famous European rival – name them.

10. In 1977, crowd trouble in the first leg in France forced United's European Cup Winners' Cup home tie with Saint-Etienne to be played at a neutral venue. At which British stadium was the second leg played?

11. Who was the first Spanish team we faced in the UEFA Cup, in 1982?

12. In 1984, United famously beat Barcelona 3-0 in the European Cup Winners' Cup quarter-final, with Bryan Robson scoring twice. Who scored the other goal?

13. What was the score in the first leg of that '84 Nou Camp tie?

14. Which European giant knocked us out of that tournament at the semi-final stage?

15. A legendary international, who was the top scorer at the 1982 World Cup, scored home and away in that semi-final – can you name him?

16. Who did we beat in the semi-finals of the 1991 European Cup Winners' Cup?

17. Two players were joint top goalscorers for United in the 1990/91 European Cup Winners' Cup, with four goals each (a defender and a forward) – can you name them?

18. Our last European Cup Winners' Cup campaign was in the 1991/92 season – can you name our final ever opponents in that tournament?

19. In total, how many seasons did we compete in the European Cup Winners' Cup?

20. How many years separated our last appearance in the UEFA Cup and our first appearance in the Europa League?

21. Who were our first Europa League opponents – a team we'd faced in the UEFA Cup?

22. In March 2012 United faced Athletic Bilbao in the Europa League – which future United player played for the Basque side?

23. And which future Premier League manager was in charge of Athletic Club for those matches?

24. Against which team did Marcus Rashford make his goalscoring debut, in the Europa League in March 2016?

25. Which former United favourite returned to Old Trafford with Fenerbahce in October 2016 and received a standing ovation when he scored his team's goal in their 4-1 defeat?

26. Which Spanish side did United beat in the semi-finals of the 2017 Europa League?

27. In 2017, United became only the fifth side to win a clean sweep of European Cup/ Champions League, UEFA Cup/ Europa League and European Cup Winners' Cup. Name the other four sides to have achieved this feat.

28. In November 2019, United fielded our youngest ever team in a European tie away to FC Astana. Which country are they from?

29. In March 2020, United played our first behind-closed-doors game away to LASK Linz in Austria. Which striker scored the opening goal in our 5-0 win?

30. The pandemic forced United to play the quarter-final and semi-final of the 2020 Europa League in which neutral city?

31. Which player scored his first goal for United with an audacious backward header against AC Milan at Old Trafford in March 2021?

32. What was the aggregate score in the 2021 Europa League semi-final against Roma?

33. Name the two ex-Reds who appeared for the opposition across that tie.

34. United drew 1-1 in the 2021 Europa League final against Villarreal, before losing on penalties. Who scored United's goal in the 90 minutes?

35. The highest scorers in UEFA Cup history and Europa League history both played for United, but never scored for the Reds in either competition. Can you name them?

OTHER EUROPEAN COMPETITIONS – WINNING FINALS

The three other prizes secured from our endeavours in Europe

THE 1991 EUROPEAN CUP WINNERS' CUP FINAL

1. Fill in the missing details in the match – opponent and the United goalscorers.

   Manchester United 2 __________ 1

   (________ 67,74 mins)

2. Fill in the missing players in the starting XI…

3. Which two United players lifted the trophy?

4. What was the venue for the final?

5. Which player, later to manage in the Premier League, scored for the opposition?

THE 1991 SUPER CUP FINAL

1. Fill in the missing details in the match – opponent and the United goalscorers.

Manchester United 1 __________ 0
(________ 67 mins)

2. Fill in the missing players in the starting XI...

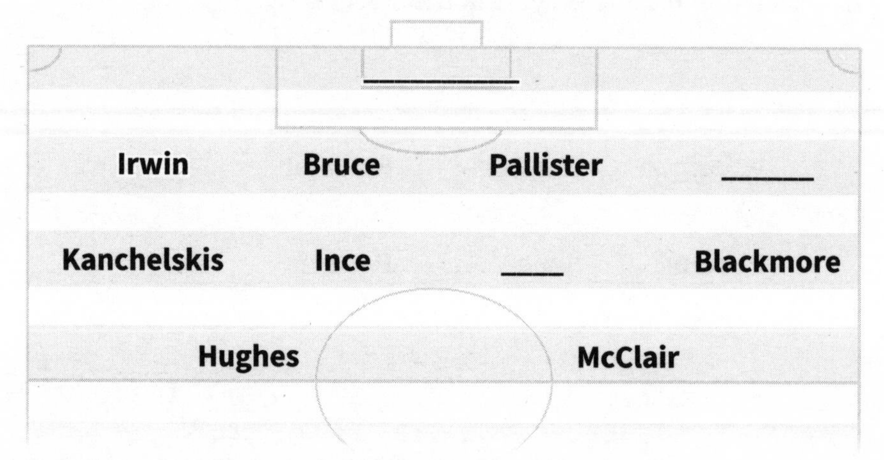

3. Who missed a penalty for United in this game?

4. What was the venue for this match?

5. In which month of the year was this match played?

THE 2017 EUROPA LEAGUE FINAL

1. Fill in the missing details in the match – opponent and the United goalscorers.

Manchester United 2 __________ 0

(________ 18 mins, __________ 48 mins)

2. Fill in the missing players in the starting XI…

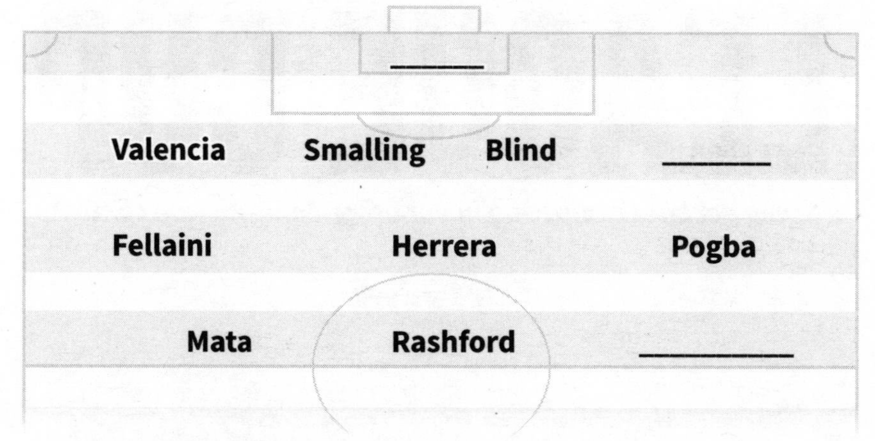

3. Which United legend came on as a sub to make his last appearance for the club?

4. Which future Red came off the bench for the opposition?

5. What was the venue for the match?

LEAGUE CUP

Seven decades competing in our other domestic cup contest

1. Name the seven title sponsors of the League Cup before it became the Carabao Cup in 2017.

2. United first competed in the League Cup in its inaugural season of 1960/61, when Matt Busby's Reds beat a side otherwise known as 'the Grecians' before being knocked out by 'the Bantams'. Can you name these two teams?

3. Our first-ever goal in the League Cup was scored by a Scottish forward, who had previously scored in our first match following the Munich Air Disaster, and who died in July 2020, aged 80. Can you name him?

4. True or false: following our second-round exit in 1960/61, United didn't progress beyond that same round of the League Cup until 1969/70.

5. Name the club we've faced in more League Cup games than any other (10 – six of which have been played since 2010).

6. Port Vale and Burnley are the teams United have beaten the most in the League Cup (six wins apiece). Which legendary Red scored a debut brace against one of these sides in the League Cup in September 1994?

7. Another club legend from that era, David Beckham, also made his Reds debut in the League Cup, in September 1992. At which away stadium in the south of the country?

8. How many League Cup finals had United competed in prior to our first success in the competition, in 1992?

9. When we won the tournament for the first time in '92, which North East team did we beat in the two-legged semi-final?

10. Who is our all-time top scorer in the competition, having netted 19 goals in 45 League Cup appearances between 1987-97.

11. And who has the most appearances for the Reds in the League Cup, with 51 between 1981-94 (scoring five goals)?

12. How many League Cup fixtures have United played at Wembley (either the original or the new stadium): seven, eight or nine?

13. When United won the competition in 2017, our road to the final consisted of victories against one 'Town' (3-1 win), a 'City' (1-0), a 'United' (4-1) and another 'City' (3-2 aggregate win in the semis). Name all four opponents.

14. In October 1976, the Reds beat Newcastle 7-2 in the competition – the most goals we've scored in a single League Cup fixture. Which winger, signed from Millwall the previous year, scored a hat-trick that night?

15. Two teams have won the League Cup at Old Trafford – in replayed finals played at a neutral venue in 1977 and 1978. Everton and Liverpool were the respective losers in those games, but can you name the winning teams?

16. Which Greater Manchester side did United beat 2-1 at Old Trafford in the fourth round of the 1987/88 League Cup – a match in which the Reds were technically the away team, with the tie switched to accommodate more supporters?

17. In 2002's League Cup quarter-final, which striker scored the only goal of the game as United beat Chelsea at Old Trafford?

18. There was another dramatic game against the Blues in this competition in the fourth round in October 2012. Can you recall the scoreline after extra-time in the Stamford Bridge clash?

19. Which future United player was in the Blues' line-up for that match?

20. Carlos Tevez scored four times in a 5-3 win over which North West side in the League Cup fifth round in December 2008?

21. A French player scored for United against Arsenal in the League Cup fifth round in December 2004, giving the Reds a 1-0 win. Name the player.

22. In 2019 we beat a team from Essex 3-0 at Old Trafford, who we last met in a competitive fixture in the League Cup in 1983 –can you name the team?

23. Paul Pogba made his senior United debut in the League Cup in September 2011 – at which ground?

24. United's goal of the season for the 2019/20 season was won for a League Cup goal. Which player scored it, and against which team?

25. Our 2021 semi-final against Manchester City ultimately saw the Blues progress, but which player scored to give us a 1-0 win in the second leg at the Etihad?

WINNING LEAGUE CUP FINALS

Five occasions the Reds have supplemented our trophy haul

THE 1992 LEAGUE CUP FINAL

1. Fill in the missing details in the match – opponent and the United goalscorer.

Manchester United 1 __________ 0

(________ 14 mins)

2. Fill in the missing players in the starting XI…

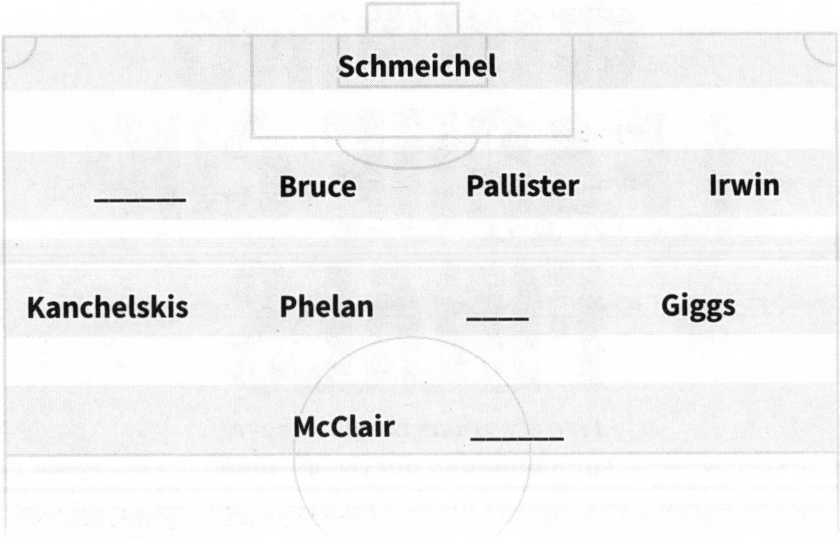

Schmeichel

______ Bruce Pallister Irwin

Kanchelskis Phelan ____ Giggs

McClair ______

3. Which two future Treble winners with United were in the opposition starting XI?

4. What was the main colour of United's kit in the final: red, blue, white or black?

5. Name the substitute who came on for Andrei Kanchelskis after 75 minutes based on these clues: he was capped eight times by England between 1991-93, and moved to Leeds in 1996 after eight years with the Reds.

THE 2006 LEAGUE CUP FINAL

1. Fill in the missing details in the match – opponent and the United goalscorer.

Manchester United 4 __________ 0

(________ 33, 61 mins, ________ 55 mins, ________ 59 mins)

2. Fill in the missing players in the starting XI…

3. In which city was the final played?

4. Who was United captain in the final?

5. Which injured team-mate did the Reds pay tribute to on their T-shirts while celebrating with the trophy?

THE 2009 LEAGUE CUP FINAL

1. Fill in the missing details in the match – opponent and full-time score before it went to penalties.

   Manchester United v __________

   Full-time score after extra-time: _ - _

2. Fill in the missing players in the starting XI…

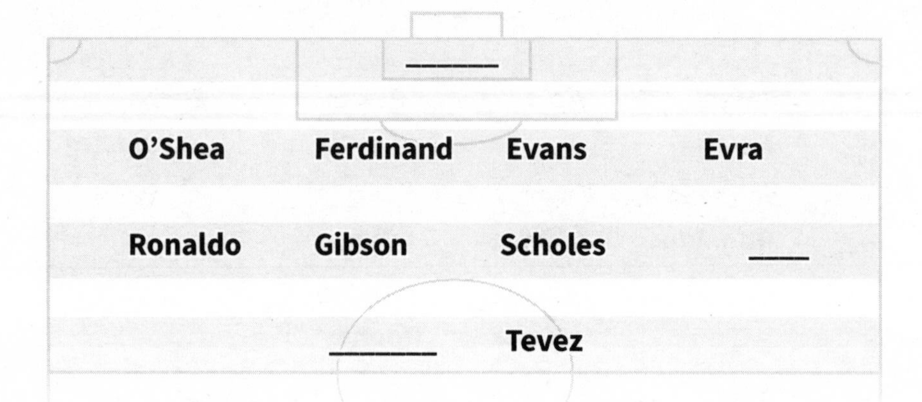

3. Name the four United penalty takers in the shoot-out, which the Reds won 4-1.

4. True or false: this was the first time the League Cup final had ever been decided by a penalty shoot-out.

5. Who was the United captain who lifted the trophy?

THE 2010 LEAGUE CUP FINAL

1. Fill in the missing details in the match – opponent and the United goalscorers.

   Manchester United 2 __________ 1
   (________ 12 mins, ________ 74 mins)

2. Fill in the missing players in the starting XI…

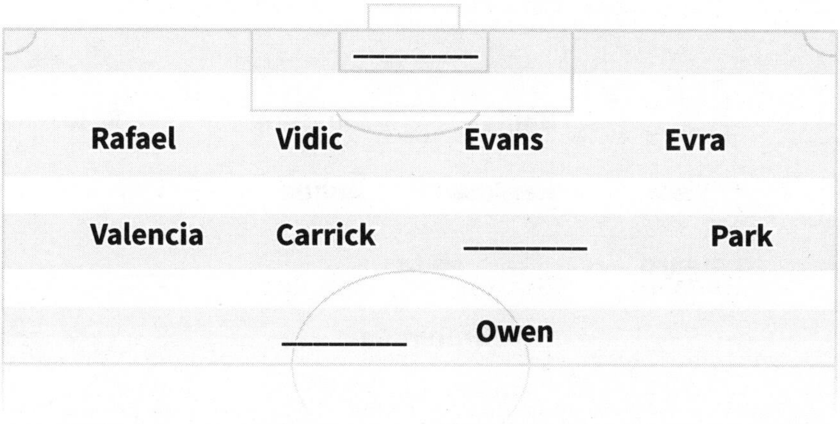

____

Rafael	Vidic	Evans	Evra
Valencia	Carrick	________	Park
	________	Owen	

3. Which future United player (who would play 261 times for the Reds, scoring 19 goals) lined up for the opposition that day?

4. Which United player gave away a fifth-minute penalty before we fought back to win the trophy?

5. True or false: this was the first time United successfully defended a major cup competition (so not including league titles)?

THE 2017 LEAGUE CUP FINAL

1. Fill in the missing details in the match – opponent and the United goalscorers.

   Manchester United 3 __________ 2
   (________ 19, 87 mins, ________ 38 mins)

2. Fill in the missing players in the starting XI…

3. True or false: this was the first time the two teams had ever met in the final of a major cup competition.

4. There was a kit clash for the final – which of the teams wore their home colours?

5. Which player, wearing the no.21 shirt, supplied the cross from the right for our headed winning goal after 87 minutes?

SIR MATT BUSBY

Test out your knowledge on our legendary trailblazer

1. In what year was Matt Busby born, to a mining family in the Scottish village of Orbiston?

2. Which Scottish team, from nearby Glasgow, did Matt grow up supporting?

3. Despite interest from clubs in Scotland, with which English club did Matt sign for as a player at the age of 18, where he would go on to play over 200 senior games?

4. Busby's one official Scotland appearance came in 1933 – against which other home nation (for whom his future assistant manager at United was playing)?

5. The highlight of Matt's club playing career was winning which trophy in 1934?

6. Who were the other English team Matt played for, after being transferred for £8,000 in 1936?

7. While at that North West club, which player did he have as a team-mate, who many years later became that same club's most successful ever manager?

8. What was the name of the United official who wrote a letter to Matt, to first suggest the possibility of becoming United manager once WWII had finished, signed 'Your old pal'?

9. What was the name of Busby's chairman at United when he joined the club?

10. Having officially begun his reign as Manchester United manager in October 1945, whom did Busby recruit as his assistant manager, a Welshman that he had faced as a player for both club and country?

11. Busby balanced his Manchester United duties in the summer of 1948 with another role – what was it?

12. To which country's domestic league did Busby lose key winger Charlie Mitten in summer 1950, earning Mitten the nickname at the time 'The Bogota Bandit'?

13. Which stalwart is Busby describing here, a player he handed a debut to in 1956? "He was a striking forward, a winger, or a deep-lying provider, always a creator of something from nothing, a player of whom the unexpected was expected, who aroused gasps of anticipation every time he had the ball."

14. In 1956 a European giant tried to lure Busby away from Manchester by offering him the role of manager. Which club was this?

15. Busby managed Scotland for two games in 1958. Which 18-year-old striker did he give his international debut to?

16. How many major trophies did United lift under Sir Matt?

17. After he had retired as Manchester United manager, what role did Busby continue to hold at the club for a number of years?

18. And what title was he given at the club in 1980?

19. What was the name of Sir Matt's beloved wife, who he was married to for 58 years?

20. In which year did Sir Matt Busby die?

21. On a highly emotional day at Old Trafford, which team provided the opposition for United's first match after Sir Matt's death?

22. What was significant about the date which would have been Sir Matt's 90th birthday?

23. In what year was Warwick Road North renamed Sir Matt Busby Way?

24. There is a banner at Old Trafford featuring a famous Sir Matt quote – complete the phrase: 'Manchester is my ______'.

25. A statue of Sir Matt Busby outside Old Trafford is located close to and faces a statue of which three United greats he managed during his reign?

SIR ALEX FERGUSON

Another legendary Scot to sit in the United hotseat, this one our longest-serving and foremost trophy collector

1. In which district of Glasgow was Alex Ferguson born, in December 1941?

2. What is his middle name?

3. With which Glasgow club did Ferguson start his football career, as a striker?

4. For his next club, St Johnstone, he scored a famous hat-trick against which Scottish team he would later join?

5. At which Scottish club, who play at Somerset Park, did Ferguson finish his playing career in 1974?

6. After retiring as a player, with which Scottish club did Ferguson begin his managerial career, at the age of 32?

7. His second managerial appointment was at a club based less than ten miles west of Glasgow. What was the name of the club, and the town where they're based?

8. With which club in Scotland did Ferguson achieve major success, including three league titles, four Scottish Cups and the European Cup Winners' Cup?

9. What was the name of the legendary manager who made Ferguson his assistant with the Scotland national team?

10. At which major tournament did Ferguson manage Scotland?

11. After being announced as Manchester United manager on 6 November 1986, at which away ground – no longer in existence – did Ferguson take charge of his first game?

12. Who did Ferguson bring from his former club to be his assistant, shortly after being named United manager?

13. Ferguson's first victory as United manager came in his third match, a 1-0 win over Queens Park Rangers at Old Trafford. Who was the Danish defender who scored the goal?

14. Who was the first player Ferguson gave a United first-team debut to, a Wigan-born goalkeeper who played for the first time in a league match at Aston Villa on 13 December 1986?

15. What position in the league table did United finish in Ferguson's first full season as Manchester United manager, 1987/88?

16. Which United great did Ferguson liken to "a cocker spaniel chasing a piece of silver paper in the wind" when he first saw him play as a youngster?

17. Which of his players was Ferguson referring to when he described a performance at Juventus in the Champions League semi-final second-leg in 1999 as "the most emphatic display of selflessness I have seen on a football field"?

18. Who was Ferguson's assistant manager in the Treble season?

19. Winning the 2008 Champions League meant Ferguson had won how many European trophies in his managerial career?

20. In which year did Sir Alex pass Sir Matt Busby's record to become United's longest-serving manager?

21. How many times was Ferguson named the Premier League Manager of the Season?

22. In which year was Sir Alex knighted?

23. Which famous American university gave Sir Alex a role as a lecturer in business and sport?

24. When was Old Trafford's North Stand renamed the Sir Alex Ferguson Stand?

25. What was the name of the film about Sir Alex's life, released in 2021?

THE PLAYERS

There's an extensive list of United greats, but here is a test of your knowledge of 30, from the early days right up to the present

WILLIAM 'BILLY' MEREDITH

1. From which club did Meredith join United in 1906?

2. Who was the manager that brought him to the Reds?

3. Billy won 49 caps representing which country?

4. What position did he primarily play across his career?

5. How many league championships did Meredith win with United?

6. Which two other trophies did he win while with the Reds?

7. Billy is often referred to as football's first superstar, but what was his nickname?

8. Meredith holds the record for being the oldest player to represent United. True or false?

9. Billy was a founder member of what longstanding organisation within English football?

10. How many games did he play for the Reds – 235, 335 or 435?

JOHN 'JACK' ROWLEY

1. From which south-coast club did United sign the forward in November 1937?

2. How many seasons did Jack play for the Reds before the outbreak of World War II?

3. During WWII, Jack guested for a number of clubs across the country, once scoring eight goals in one game for Wolves against Derby. True or false?

4. Due the explosive power of his shooting, what nickname did the striker earn?

5. How many goals did he score in the 1948 FA Cup final against Blackpool?

6. His highest goal return for a season was 30. Did he achieve that once, twice or three times for United?

7. The Reds clinched the first league title of the Matt Busby era in 1951/52 with a 6-1 home win against Arsenal in the final match of the season. How many goals did Rowley score in that game?

8. At international level he scored six goals in six games for which country?

9. How many goals did Jack score for United in his career – 191, 211, 221?

10. Which club from the Netherlands did he go on to manage, from 1963-64?

JOHNNY CAREY

1. In what year did the Dublin-born defender join the Reds from St James' Gate for £200 – 1935, 1936 or 1937?

2. How many trophies did Carey win as a United player?

3. Which individual player award did Johnny win in 1949 – the PFA Player of the Year or the Football Writers' Association Player of the Year?

4. Johnny's first season in the United first team resulted in the Reds achieving what in 1937/38?

5. At the resumption of league football after World War II, Carey was chosen by new Reds manager Matt Busby as club captain. For how many seasons did he hold the role – six, seven or eight?

6. What position did Carey play against Sunderland on 18 February 1953?

7. True or false? Johnny represented both the Republic of Ireland and Northern Ireland at international level?

8. Did Carey play more games at Old Trafford or United's temporary post-War home, Maine Road?

9. Did Carey make 244, 344 or 444 competitive appearances for United?

10. Which Lancashire club did the Irishman join as manager after hanging up his boots in the summer of 1953 – Blackpool, Burnley or Blackburn Rovers?

DUNCAN EDWARDS

1. In which West Midlands town was Duncan Edwards born on 1 October 1936?

2. Edwards made his United debut in a First Division fixture in 1952/53 against which Welsh club – Cardiff City, Swansea City or Wrexham?

3. Duncan won three FA Youth Cups with United, but what were the years of those successes?

4. The United man made his international debut for England on 2 April 1955 at Wembley. Name the Three Lions' opponent in that Home Championship match.

5. Which nation's press nicknamed him 'Boom Boom' after he'd scored with a ferocious shot against their side in an international friendly for England on 26 May 1956?

6. Against which Lancashire club did 'Big Dunc' score his first senior goal for the Reds on New Year's Day 1955 – Blackburn Rovers, Blackpool, or Burnley?

7. How many senior trophies did Edwards win with United?

8. Against which club did the half-back play his final domestic match for United, opening the scoring in a nine-goal thriller?

9. Which of his United and England team-mates famously said of Duncan: "He was the only player who made me feel inferior."

10. How old was Edwards when he tragically died of injuries sustained in the Munich Air Disaster – 20, 21 or 22?

TOMMY TAYLOR

1. From which club did United sign Taylor in March 1953?

2. For what memorable fee did the striker make the transfer to Old Trafford?

3. How old was he when he signed for United?

4. Did he win his first England cap before or after joining United?

5. Taylor scored twice on his Reds debut, but against which Lancashire club – Blackburn Rovers, Blackpool, or Preston North End?

6. Matt Busby's side famously beat Anderlecht 10-0 in the European Cup at Maine Road in 1956. How many goals did the Yorkshireman score against the Belgians that night?

7. Tommy scored an 80th-minute winner against which club to clinch the Busby Babes' first league championship on 7 April 1956 – Chelsea, Wolves or Blackpool?

8. True or false? Taylor scored 16 goals in 19 games for England.

9. The striker scored one goal for United at Wembley, but who was it against?

10. Tommy was one of the eight players tragically killed in the Munich Air Disaster, but which appearances/goals total is correct for him – 151 apps/101 goals, 191 apps/131 goals or 291 apps/231 goals?

BILL FOULKES

1. What profession did William Anthony 'Bill' Foulkes undertake prior to joining United as a trainee in March 1950?

2. Was Bill a defender, midfielder or a forward during his playing career?

3. Against which Merseyside club did Foulkes make his senior debut on 13 December 1952?

4. Bill won a solitary international cap for which home nation in October 1954?

5. Munich survivor Foulkes famously captained United against which club in the first match after the tragic plane crash?

6. Bill was one of only two players to appear in the last game before the Munich Air Disaster and the first game afterward it. Name the other.

7. Against which club did Foulkes score the third goal in a title-clinching 6-1 rout on 6 May 1967?

8. Which trophy is missing from the impressive list of honours won by Foulkes across his lengthy United career? First Division (x4), European Cup (x1), ______ (x1), Charity Shield (x3)

9. What was the significance of Bill scoring against Real Madrid in the European Cup on 15 May 1968?

10. What was Foulkes's final total for appearances and goals for United – 588 apps/9 goals, 688 apps/9 goals or 788 apps/9 goals?

BOBBY CHARLTON

1. Charlton scored two goals on his United debut (6 October 1956), but against which London club?

2. How many FA Youth Cup wins did Sir Bobby enjoy with United?

3. Which season was Charlton's most prolific for the Reds – 1958/59, 1959/60 or 1960/61?

4. Sir Bobby won the first of his 106 England caps on 19 April 1958 against Scotland. But against which country did he win his final cap?

5. How many goals did he score in the 1968 European Cup final against Benfica?

6. In what year did Charlton win the *Ballon d'Or*?

7. Against which club did Charlton play his final competitive United match, on 28 April 1973?

8. After leaving United, Charlton became manager of which North West club?

9. What position in the Reds' all-time appearance rankings does Sir Bobby currently hold?

10. How many goals did Charlton score for United?

DENIS LAW

1. In which Scottish city was Law born?

2. From which Italian club did United sign the Scotsman for £115,000 in August 1962?

3. And which two English clubs had Law previously played for before moving to Italy?

4. In what year did he win the *Ballon d'Or*?

5. Law scored four times in a game for the Reds on four occasions. Name any one of the sides he did that against.

6. How many statues does Law have at Old Trafford?

7. What nickname did United fans call him by during his 11 years at Old Trafford?

8. Which of the following games/goals tallies is the correct one for Denis at United – 404 apps/237 goals, 424 apps/237 goals or 454 apps/237 goals?

9. Law still holds the record for most goals in a season (all competitions). But what is the total – 45, 46 or 47?

10. Denis jointly holds the record for most international goals for Scotland (30) with which player?

GEORGE BEST

1. In what city was Best born on 22 May 1946?

2. George made his United debut on 14 September 1963, but against which Midlands club?

3. What was the first senior honour of Best's career?

4. How many matches did George Best miss in all competitions in the 1964/65 season – none, one or two?

5. The Portuguese press nicknamed him 'El Beatle' after a stunning display helped the Reds to a 5-1 hammering of Benfica in Estadio da Luz in March 1966. How many goals did he score in that game?

6. In what year did he win the *Ballon d'Or*?

7. Against which London club did Best make his final United appearance on New Year's Day 1974?

8. Did Best play 460, 470 or 480 times for Manchester United (scoring 179 goals)?

9. Which London club did he play for later in his career?

10. Which trophy is missing from Best's list of honours won as a Manchester United player? First Division (x2), European Cup (x1), ______ (x2)

MARTIN BUCHAN

1. Which United manager signed the defender from Aberdeen for £125,000 on 29 February 1972?

2. True or false? Martin's brother George also played for United in 1973/74.

3. What was notable about Buchan's Scottish Cup win with Aberdeen in 1970 and the Reds' FA Cup triumph in 1977?

4. What trophy did Martin lift with the Reds in 1975?

5. Martin famously released a record in 1976 about his United team-mates, entitled *The Old Trafford* _____. Complete the song title.

6. Martin scored four goals for United. Name any one of the four teams he scored against.

7. Buchan played under four Manchester United managers – who were they?

8. How many times did the Scotland international appear at Wembley with United?

9. Buchan made how many appearances for United – 456 or 465?

10. To which Greater Manchester club did Martin move on a free transfer in the summer of 1983?

STEVE COPPELL

1. From which club did United sign the winger in February 1975?

2. Under which manager did Coppell make the majority of his 396 United appearances – Tommy Docherty, Dave Sexton, or Ron Atkinson?

3. Was Steve primarily a winger on the right or left flank?

4. What shirt number did Coppell wear most often across his nine seasons as a Red?

5. True or false? The Liverpool-born winger played in a remarkable 206 consecutive league matches for United, from 15 January 1977 to 7 November 1981.

6. Did Coppell appear for England more or fewer times than fellow Reds winger Gordon Hill?

7. The winger appeared at Wembley five times with United; how many of those matches did he win?

8. A Spanish club provided the opposition for Coppell's testimonial match in 1986, after he'd been forced to retire through injury aged 28, but was it Real Madrid, Deportivo La Coruna or Real Sociedad who provided the opposition?

9. Did Steve score 60, 70 or 80 goals for United across his career?

10. Which club did Coppell later manage against United in the 1990 FA Cup final?

BRYAN ROBSON

1. Who described Robson as "pure gold" upon the midfielder switching from West Bromwich Albion to Manchester United?

2. Against which club did he make his Reds debut on 7 October 1981 in a League Cup tie?

3. Robbo enjoyed his most prolific season in 1983/84, but did he score 17, 18 or 19 goals?

4. Bryan won nine trophies as a United player, but which one is missing from this list? Premier League (x2), FA Cup (x3), League Cup (x1), Charity Shield (x2), ________ (x1)

5. How many caps did Robson win for England – 80, 90 or 100?

6. And how many goals did he score for United?

7. Robbo represented United at Wembley on 10 occasions. How many times did he win?

8. And how many goals did he score across those 10 Wembley visits?

9. Against which club did Bryan score his final goal for the Reds – Manchester City, Everton or Oldham Athletic?

10. To which club did Robson move in 1994, to become their player-manager?

NORMAN WHITESIDE

1. In what city was Whiteside born on 7 May 1965?

2. What was Big Norm's other nickname, inspired by the road he grew up on?

3. Norman scored his first goal for the Reds aged 17 years and eight days. Against which club did his maiden goal come – Southampton, Brighton & Hove Albion, or Stoke City?

4. Fresh from his club breakthrough, the striker was promptly selected for Northern Ireland's squad for the Spain 82 World Cup. Who was the player whose record he broke by becoming the youngest player to appear at a World Cup finals?

5. Whiteside scored one hat-trick for the Reds, but which side did it come against?

6. Against which club did he score the winning goal at Villa Park in the semi-final of the 1983 FA Cup?

7. The Northern Irishman played for United in six different competitions; which two are missing from this list? First Division, FA Cup, League Cup, Charity Shield, _______ and ________

8. Norman scored a stunning 78th-minute winner against Liverpool on Boxing Day 1986 in Alex Ferguson's first game against the Merseysiders, but was it at Old Trafford or Anfield?

9. “As a player, he was close to the genius category.” Who famously gave this glowing appraisal of Whiteside?

10. To which North West club did the Northern Irishman move in July 1989?

MARK HUGHES

1. Against which club did Sparky make his United debut in the League Cup on 26 October 1983 – Port Vale or Oxford United?

2. Hughes scored the winning goal for Wales against England on his international debut, on 2 May 1984. The game was played in his hometown, but name the stadium.

3. The Welshman scored four hat-tricks for United across his two spells at the club. Name any one of the clubs he scored a treble against.

4. Sparky left the Reds to join Barcelona in summer 1986, but at which other club did he play prior to re-joining United in June 1988?

5. Hughes won 11 trophies as a United player, but which one is missing from this list? Premier League (x2), FA Cup (x3), League Cup (x1), Charity Shield (x3), European Cup Winners' Cup (x1), ________ (x1)

6. Which season was Mark's most prolific for United – 1984/85, 1990/91 or 1993/94?

7. Hughes was always the man for the big occasion, but how many times did he score for United at Wembley?

8. What was notable about the Welshman's goal at Bramall Lane on 15 August 1992?

9. How many finals did Hughes score in for the Reds (in all comps)?

10. Against which club did Sparky play his final competitive game for United on 20 May 1995? (*Hint: he later played for them).*

DENIS IRWIN

1. From which club did the Reds sign the Irishman in June 1990, for £250,000?

2. Against which club did Denis make his United debut on 18 August 1990?

3. Irwin netted his first goal for the Reds in his second season. Against which club with a bird-related nickname did he open his account – Norwich City, Newcastle United or Crystal Palace?

4. Denis played 62 out of 63 matches in what successful season for United – 1992/93, 1993/94 or 1998/99?

5. The Irishman was the designated penalty taker for periods of his United career, scoring from the spot 12 times. Name either of the two clubs he netted a penalty against more than once.

6. How many World Cups did Denis play in with Ireland, for whom he won 56 caps?

7. Denis was sent off just once in his United career, but against which club?

8. The full-back was twice named in the PFA Team of the Year for the Premier League. Name one of the two seasons.

9. Irwin played his final United game against Charlton Athletic at Old Trafford, but in what season – 2001/02, 2002/03 or 2003/04?

10. Which honour is missing from Denis's impressive haul of 18 trophies as a Red? Premier League (x7), FA Cup (x2), League Cup (x1), Charity Shield (x4), European Cup (1), European Cup Winners' Cup (x1), Super Cup (x1) and ________ (x1)

PETER SCHMEICHEL

1. True or false: the Danish goalkeeper was the Reds' only signing of summer 1991?

2. How many trophies did Schmeichel win with club and country in the calendar year 1992?

3. What is Peter's middle name – Boleslaw or Gladsaxe?

4. Against which two London clubs did Schmeichel appear most often for United – Arsenal and Tottenham, Tottenham and Chelsea, or Arsenal and Chelsea?

5. The Dane holds the record for most clean sheets in United's history, but how many did he achieve – 150, 180 or 200?

6. How many Premier League titles did Peter win with the Reds?

7. Against which club did Schmeichel score his only goal for United, becoming our first keeper to score from open play?

8. What was the first of the 15 trophies he won with United?

9. Against which opposition club was his final Premier League away game as a Manchester United player?

10. To which club did Schmeichel move in the summer of 1999?

ERIC CANTONA

1. Which English club initially brought Cantona to England on trial, before he signed for Leeds United?

2. What number was Cantona wearing on his back the day he made his Manchester United debut?

3. And who were the opposition that day?

4. Eric's first United goal came against which London club on 19 December 1992?

5. The Frenchman was named Sir Matt Busby Player of the Year twice in his United career. Can you name either one of those two seasons?

6. In what year did Eric finish third in the voting for the *Ballon d'Or* – 1993 or 1996?

7. Eric won nine trophies with the Reds, but which of these did he not win – Premier League, FA Cup, League Cup, Charity Shield?

8. Name either the player who wore United's no.7 shirt prior to Eric or the player who wore it after him.

9. Eric Cantona was suspended for eight months after attacking a Crystal Palace supporter at Selhurst Park in January 1995. Against which side was his first away match upon his return? *(Hint: it was a League Cup tie).*

10. True or false? Eric retired from football aged 30, playing his last competitive game against Watford on 11 May 1997?

ROY KEANE

1. Which piece of the following information from Keane's home debut is incorrect? United 3 (Keane 16, 43; Cantona 85) Sheffield United 0, Premier League, 18 August 1993

2. Roy scored twice against which club on his Champions League debut for United? *(Hint: they are Hungarian)*.

3. What shirt number did Keane wear in the Premier League for the full duration of his United career?

4. How many trophies did Keano win as a Red – 13, 15 or 17?

5. True or false? Keane won back-to-back Sir Matt Busby Player of the Year awards in 1999 and 2000.

6. In which of those years was he also named PFA and Football Writers' Player of the Year?

7. Name either the player who preceded Keano as United club captain or the player who succeeded him.

8. Against which club did the Irishman score the only goal to win the Intercontinental Cup on 30 November 1999?

9. Did Keano make 470, 480 or 490 United appearances?

10. At which club did Roy play after leaving Manchester United in 2005?

RYAN GIGGS

1. Against which club did Giggs make his United debut, on 2 March 1991?

2. And which club did he score his first Reds goal against, on 4 May 1991?

3. Which was the first of these three trophies that Ryan won in his career – the FA Youth Cup, UEFA Super Cup, or the League Cup?

4. In what year was Giggs voted the Sir Matt Busby Player of the Year?

5. True or false? Ryan Giggs is the only player to have winner's medals for all 13 of United's Premier League titles.

6. How many first-team trophies did Ryan win with the Reds – 30, 32 or 34?

7. Giggs won a car for being named Man of the Match in the 1999 Intercontinental Cup final, but what object was he presented with to mark the award?

8. In which fixture did the winger overtake Sir Bobby Charlton to become the club's all-time leading appearance maker?

9. Against which club did Giggs make his 963rd and final United appearance on 6 May 2014?

10. Ryan scored 168 goals for the Reds, including 10 against two different clubs – one from the North East, the other from London. Name either of them.

GARY NEVILLE

1. Did Gary win six, seven or eight Premier League titles across his United career?

2. Neville scored seven goals across his United career. Name two of the clubs he scored against.

3. Who were the opposition when Gary first appeared alongside his brother Phil for United at senior level, on 7 May 1995 – Sheffield United, Sheffield Wednesday or Bradford City?

4. Against which club did 'Red Nev' make his final United appearance on New Year's Day 2011? *(Clue: they play in stripes)*.

5. What was the first trophy Gary won after being made United's captain?

6. True or false? Only three players appeared more times for the Reds in the Treble season (1998/99) than Gary, who played in 54 of our 63 matches.

7. Did Gary win more FA Cups or League Cups during his United career?

8. Gary won 85 caps for England, but at how many World Cups did he appear for the Three Lions – one, two or three?

9. Which Italian club provided the opposition for Neville's testimonial match, played on 24 May 2011?

10. Did Gary play 602, 652 or 702 times for United?

DAVID BECKHAM

1. True or false? David Beckham scored on his United debut against Galatasaray, on 7 December 1994.

2. Becks scored from the halfway line against Wimbledon, at Selhurst Park, but what season was that – 1995/96, 1996/97 or 1997/98?

3. Against which club did Beckham score his first Premier League goal?

4. Beckham wore the no.7 shirt from season 1997/98 to 2002/03. Name any three of the Premier League squad numbers he wore prior to that.

5. In what season did David finish second in the voting for the *Ballon d'Or* – 1998, 1999 or 2000?

6. Becks scored 27 direct free-kicks for United, six of them in the Champions League. Which of these continental clubs did he NOT score a free-kick against – Barcelona, Brondby, Croatia Zagreb, Nantes, Zalaegerszeg, Deportivo La Coruna or Real Madrid?

7. Becks scored seven goals against which two London clubs?

8. How many FA Cup and League Cup finals did David appear in?

9. Beckham won 115 caps for England, 60 of which were as a United player. Name two of the other three other clubs with whom he won his other 55 caps?

10. Which famous European club did he play his last professional match for?

PAUL SCHOLES

1. Against which club did Paul Scholes make his United debut, on 21 September 1994?

2. Scholes scored two hat-tricks for the Reds in his career, but which of these three clubs did he NOT score a hat-trick against – Barnsley, West Ham or Newcastle?

3. How many Premier League titles did the midfielder win?

4. And how many FA Cups?

5. Scholes wore shirt no.18 for most of his United career, but what number did he wear in his second spell with the Reds? *(Hint: It's the same number that he'd previously worn in 1995/96).*

6. Scholesy famously scored the winning goal against Barcelona in the Champions League semi-final second leg at Old Trafford, on 29 April 2008 – but which goalkeeper did he score past?

7. In 2019 Scholes had a short spell managing which North West club?

8. Which London club did Paul face more than any other across his Reds career – Arsenal, Chelsea, or Tottenham?

9. One of the highlights of the midfielder's 66-game England career was scoring both goals in a 2-0 victory against which other home nation, on 13 November 1999?

10. Did Scholes make 618 United appearances, 718 appearances or 818 appearances?

OLE GUNNAR SOLSKJAER

1. Ole Gunnar Solskjaer was signed from which Norwegian club in summer 1996?

2. How many goals did he score on his United debut against Blackburn Rovers in a 2-2 draw, on 25 August 1996?

3. The Norwegian scored three hat-tricks during his United career, but against which of these teams did he NOT collect the match ball – Nottingham Forest, Tottenham Hotspur, Everton or Bolton Wanderers?

4. The media and fans often referred to Ole by a nickname given to him for his looks and his lethal finishing, but what was it?

5. True or false? Ole replaced Jesper Blomqvist in the 67th minute of the Champions League final against Bayern Munich, at the Nou Camp on 26 May 1999.

6. Name two of the other four Norwegians to have represented United (prior to the end of the 2021/22 season).

7. How many goals did Ole score for United – 96, 126 or 156?

8. Which honour is missing from Solskjaer's impressive haul of trophies as a Red? Premier League (x6), FA Cup (x2), ________ (x2), Champions League (x1), Intercontinental Cup (x1)

9. Which Spanish club provided the opposition for Solskjaer's testimonial match on 2 August 2008 – Real Sociedad, Real Betis, or Espanyol?

10. Solskjaer left his job as manager of Molde to take over as boss of which club in 2014?

RUUD VAN NISTELROOY

1. True or false? Ruud was the first player to join United from PSV Eindhoven, signing for the Reds in July 2001.

2. Against which club did van Nistelrooy score on his Manchester United debut – Liverpool or Fulham?

3. Which of Ruud's five seasons at Old Trafford was his most prolific for the Reds – 2001/02, 2002/03 or 2003/04?

4. The Dutchman netted six hat-tricks during his United career, with one being a four-goal haul – but who was that against?

5. What club scoring record does van Nistelrooy hold? *(Hint: he's one ahead of Wayne Rooney)*

6. Ruud wore the same number shirt for all five seasons he was a Red. What number was that?

7. Van Nistelrooy impressively won each of English football's major honours once, but what are the two missing years from the following list – Premier League (2002/03), FA Cup (______), League Cup (_____), Community Shield (2003)?

8. The striker scored a neat round number of goals for United, but was that 100, 150 or 200 goals?

9. Name two of the three clubs Ruud played for after leaving the Reds in July 2006.

10. In March 2022 it was announced that Ruud would become the new head coach of which Dutch side?

RIO FERDINAND

1. True or false? In the years before joining United, Rio was part of a West Ham team on the receiving end of a 7-1 Premier League thumping at Old Trafford.

2. Against which Hungarian club with an unusual name did the defender make his first United appearance?

3. Ferdinand scored eight goals for the Reds against seven different clubs, but who did he score against twice in his United career?

4. How many league titles did Ferdinand win as a Red – five, six or seven?

5. Which domestic honour did Ferdinand not win during his 12 seasons at Old Trafford?

6. The defender won 81 caps for England, but how many World Cup finals did he appear at – one, two or three?

7. What is the name of Rio's footballing brother?

8. Ferdinand scored the winning goal against which club in Sir Alex Ferguson's last home game as United manager?

9. What shirt number did Rio wear for just one season, in 2002/03?

10. Which London club did Rio join after leaving United in 2014?

NEMANJA VIDIC

1. From which club did United sign Nemanja on 6 January 2006 – Red Star Belgrade, Benfica, or Spartak Moscow?

2. The Serbian joined United four days before Patrice Evra – but which of the new signings was first to make their debut?

3. What was Nemanja's nickname among his team-mates – 'Viva', 'Viba' or 'Vida'?

4. Which Chelsea player was shown a red card for slapping Vidic in the second half of extra-time in the 2008 Champions League final in Moscow?

5. Against which club did the defender score a consolation goal in United's 1-2 UEFA Super Cup defeat in Monaco in August 2008?

6. At the 2008 FIFA Club World Cup in Japan, Vidic scored against which Japanese club at the semi-final stage?

7. And against which club did Nemanja receive a red card in the final of the FIFA Club World Cup, a game United went on to win 1-0?

8. Was Vidic Manchester United captain from 2007-10, 2009-2012, or 2011-14?

9. The Serbian played a round number of games for United across his nine seasons – but is that 250, 300 or 350 games?

10. To which Italian club did Vidic move on a free transfer in July 2014 – AC Milan, Juventus or Internazionale?

CRISTIANO RONALDO

1. Which Portuguese club did United sign Ronaldo from?

2. Against which club did the Portuguese make his United debut at Old Trafford on 16 August 2003?

3. And against which club did he score his first United goal – Portsmouth, Manchester City or Tottenham Hotspur?

4. United's no.7 scored United's goal in the 2008 Champions League final in Moscow, but who crossed the ball for his powerful header?

5. In what year was Ronaldo named both *Ballon d'Or* winner and FIFA World Player of the Year while with the Reds?

6. In which of these seasons was Cristiano NOT named Sir Matt Busby Player of the Year – 2003/04, 2006/07, 2007/08 and 2008/09?

7. Did the Portuguese win more league titles while a Red, or with Real Madrid or Juventus?

8. Which fellow former United team-mate was in the starting line-up for Portugal in the 2016 European Championship final?

9. Cristiano returned to United in August 2021, but how many goals did he score in our 2021/22 Champions League campaign?

10. Ronaldo scored the third hat-trick of his United career (and the second in his second spell) against which club?

WAYNE ROONEY

1. Against which Turkish club did Rooney score a hat-trick on his United debut on 28 September 2004?

2. The striker bagged eight hat-tricks in all for the Reds, six of them in the Premier League. But which two clubs are missing from this list of sides he scored league triples (or more) against – Bolton Wanderers (twice), __________, Hull City, ________ and Arsenal?

3. For how many seasons did he wear the no.8 shirt for the Reds, before moving to wear no.10?

4. True or false? Rooney scored five times against his former club Everton across his United career, but only one of those goals was at Goodison Park.

5. In what season was Rooney named both PFA and Football Writers' Association Player of the Year?

6. Wayne was club captain at Old Trafford from 2014-2017, but how many trophies did he win during that period?

7. Rooney won 120 caps for England, scoring 53 goals, with 17 of those appearances coming with Everton and 102 with United. At which club was he playing when he won his final cap for the Three Lions?

8. Wazza is United's all-time leading goalscorer with how many goals – 252, 253 or 254?

9. Rooney played 559 times for United, with 402 of those under Sir Alex Ferguson. But did he play more matches for Louis van Gaal or Jose Mourinho?

10. With which club did Rooney begin his managerial career?

DAVID DE GEA

1. In which city was De Gea born?

2. He won a trophy in his first match for United, the 2011 Community Shield. Who did United play that day?

3. And who was his Premier League debut against?

4. In what season did the Spaniard win the Premier League Golden Glove for most clean sheets in a season (18) – 2017/18 or 2018/19?

5. In which year did De Gea make his senior debut for Spain?

6. How many titles had De Gea won up to the end of the 2021/22 season?

7. David saved a penalty in United's FA Cup semi-final against Everton on 23 April 2016, but which player did he deny?

8. De Gea has faced nine Spanish teams so far with the Reds. Name the two clubs missing from this list of opponents: Atletico Madrid, Athletic Club, Barcelona, _______, Real Madrid, Real Sociedad, Sevilla, Valencia, _______

9. True or false? Alex Stepney and Peter Schmeichel are the only goalkeepers to have played for United more times than David.

10. In how many finals had De Gea played up to the end of the '21/22 season (excluding Super Cups and Community Shields)?

BRUNO FERNANDES

1. From which club did Bruno join the Reds in January 2020?

2. He made his debut on 1 February 2020 in a Premier League match at Old Trafford against which club?

3. Against which club did Bruno score his first United goal from open play?

4. The Portuguese was named Sir Matt Busby Player of the Year for 2019/20, but who finished closest behind him in the vote – Marcus Rashford, Harry Maguire or Anthony Martial?

5. Against which south-coast club did Fernandes score with the last kick of the match on 26 September 2020?

6. What number shirt does the Portuguese wear for United?

7. Against which club did Bruno score Manchester United's 2020/21 goal of the season, voted for by fans on the club's app and website – Everton, Southampton, or Liverpool?

8. At the end of the 2020/21 season, Fernandes retained the Sir Matt Busby Player of the Year. But who was second behind him in the voting – David De Gea, Luke Shaw, or Alex Telles?

9. What competition did Bruno win with Portugal in 2018/19?

10. Who did Bruno score a hat-trick against on 14 August 2021?

MANCHESTER UNITED WOMEN

Formed in 2018, it's been an thrilling ascent for our other senior side

1. Which stadium hosted Manchester United Women's first-ever competitive game, away to Liverpool in August 2018?

2. Name the three players in the United starting XI that day who had joined from Liverpool that summer.

3. How many different players found the net for the Reds in the club's first-ever league outing, a 12-0 triumph away to Aston Villa?

4. Just one of United's first 47 games finished as a draw – who were the opposition?

5. Who were the only two away sides to score at Leigh Sports Village in the league during 2018/19?

6. The Reds' first game of 2019, at home to London Bees, was a club-record Championship victory at Leigh Sports Village, but what was the final score?

7. Which south-coast team were United's first-ever FA Cup opponents?

8. The club's first Continental League Cup campaign came to an end against Arsenal in February 2019 at which stage of the competition?

9. Which defender broke the deadlock in a 5-0 win at home to Aston Villa in April 2019 as United clinched promotion to the Women's Super League?

10. Who finished as top scorer in United's maiden campaign, with 18 goals across all competitions?

11. The Reds' first top-flight strike was scored by which player?

12. Who was the first of United's 2019 summer signings to get on the scoresheet, the Scottish striker doing so in a 3-0 win away to Spurs in October?

13. A first derby victory also came in October 2019, in the Continental League Cup, but along with United and City, who were the other three sides in Group C?

14. Who became the first United star to win the WSL Player of the Month award after her performances in October 2019?

15. November's 11-1 success at home to Leicester saw Ella Toone score how many goals, to equal the record set by Jess Sigsworth for the most by a Red in a single game?

16. Who were the first club to face United at least once in each of the Women's Super League, the FA Cup and the Continental League Cup?

17. As previously mentioned, there was just one draw among the first 47 fixtures, before back-to-back stalemates in February 2020 – what was the final score in both games?

18. Who were United's final opponents before the 2019/20 WSL season was brought to an early end?

19. And which Reds forward scored her first WSL goal in that fixture?

20. The final table was calculated on a points-per-game basis – within 0.1, how many PPG did Casey Stoney's team receive?

21. Who became the player to reach 50 appearances for the Reds, doing so in the 2020/21 opener at home to Chelsea?

22. Which club did United face for the first time in the league in September 2020, with both of the previous season's scheduled meetings having been postponed?

23. US superstars Tobin Heath and Christen Press both opened their scoring accounts for the Reds against which London side?

24. United's first penalty shoot-out came against Manchester City, in which competition?

25. The calendar year of 2020 ended with a 6-1 WSL success against which club?

26. Which Norwegian became the club's first-ever January signing, at the beginning of 2021?

27. Kirsty Hanson netted the 100th United goal at Leigh Sports Village on 7 March 2021 when she opened the scoring against which team?

28. What was the final score when United took on West Ham in the women's team's first game at Old Trafford?

29. The 2020/21 FA Cup journey began against which club – the first non-league side United had faced in a competitive fixture?

30. Casey Stoney's final game in charge was at home to which side?

31. Who scored both United's final WSL goal of 2020/21 as well as the first league strike of the following season?

32. What was the final score in Marc Skinner's first competitive match as United manager?

33. Which two Reds hit international hat-tricks for England in 2021?

34. In which months did Skinner win consecutive WSL Manager of the Month awards?

35. And which Reds claimed the Player of the Month prizes in the same period?

36. Signe Bruun became United's first-ever loan signing in January 2022, arriving from which French side?

37. Which youngster and daughter of a Treble winner made her debut as a substitute against Bridgwater United in the FA Cup?

38. Which player scored three times direct from corners in back-to-back games across February and March 2022?

39. Within 1,000, what was the attendance for the women's team's first Old Trafford game in front of fans?

40. Who was the only player to feature in every one of United's WSL games in the team's first three top-flight campaigns?

41. Name the first three winners of United's Player of the Year award.

42. As of the end of the 2021/22 season, which two teams have United faced most often in competitive fixtures, playing each 10 times?

43. After England and Scotland, which nation has had the most players to make a first-team appearance for United as of the end of 2021/22, with four?

44. Who was the first United debutant whose first game was NOT in the club's opening fixture away to Liverpool?

45. Ella Toone became the first Red to reach 100 club appearances but, as of the end of 2021/22, who is next closest to reaching the milestone?

46. Which two players to have ever represented United scored at the 2019 World Cup?

47. As of the end of 2021/22, which is the furthest stage United have reached in the FA Cup?

48. Who were the opponents in the Reds' 100th competitive game, in March 2022?

49. Other than Leigh Sports Village and Old Trafford, in which other stadium have United played a competitive 'home' game?

50. Who was the first United player to score exactly three goals in a game?

HAT-TRICKS

It's one of football's most celebrated achievements – test your knowledge of the times players took home the match ball after stealing the show...

1. Which player has scored the most hat-tricks for United in the club's history?

2. Only two players have scored hat-tricks on their United debut. Wayne Rooney was one of them – can you name the other?

3. Name the two United players to have scored 'double hat-tricks' for the Reds (ie six goals in one game).

4. Who scored more hat-tricks for United – Wayne Rooney or Ruud van Nistelrooy?

5. Who was the first overseas player to score a hat-trick for United?

6. Cristiano Ronaldo only scored one hat-trick in his first spell with United – against which club, and in which season?

7. Which player scored his one and only hat-trick for the club against Norwich City in March 2013?

8. Name the three clubs Robin van Persie scored hat-tricks against in United colours.

9. Which former United player is the only one to have scored Premier League hat-tricks for three different clubs?

10. It took until November 1994 for United to register a hat-trick in the Premier League. Who scored it, and against which team?

11. Two players scored hat-tricks in the behind-closed-doors matches of 2020, one in the league and one in Europe. Name the players and the opposition.

12. Two players scored hat-tricks or better in United's record 10-0 victory over Anderlecht in the 1957 European Cup tie – who were they?

13. The same striker scored our last hat-trick in the 1970s (against Leeds), and the first hat-trick of the 1980s (against Spurs). Name the player.

14. Zlatan Ibrahimovic scored one hat-trick for the Reds, against a team he had faced in domestic competition on the continent. Against whom?

15. Against which team did United players score home-and-away hat-tricks in the 2002/03 Premier League season?

16. Which Englishman scored the most hat-tricks for United?

17. Two United players have scored Premier League hat-tricks against Arsenal – who are they?

18. Who did Michael Owen score an away Champions League hat-trick against?

19. Two players went two better than a hat-trick in the Premier League with five goals in one game. Name the players and the opposition.

20. Dimitar Berbatov scored a hat-trick against Liverpool in 2010, the first against our old rivals in nearly 60 years. Which player scored that previous hat-trick v Liverpool?

Here are the top 25 all-time appearance-makers and goalscorers in the club's history, in order. Only thing is, we've mixed up their names. Can you decipher the anagrams and name the players?

TOP 25 APPEARANCE-MAKERS

A. 1. SAGGY GRIN

B. 2. BROTH CAN LOBBY

C. 3. SHELLAC OPUS

D. 4. SO ILK BE FULL

E. 5. REVEALINGLY

F. 6. YO WEARY NEON

G. 7. PENALTY EXES

H. 8. TEND YO NUN

I. 9. WIN INSIDER

J. 10. JEEP SCONE

K. 11. A TRIATHLON RUBS

L. 12. DIVE AGE ADD

M. 13. KENYA ORE

N. 14. CRIMINAL CRAB

O. 15. ROB TEES EGG

P. 16. MR HUSH A KEG

Q. 17. ACHIER ARM CLICK

R. 18. RAN BONY ORBS

S. 19. CABIN HAUNT MR

T. 20. REF IN ANDROID

U. 21. CLICKS A JOCK

V. 22. SPIRAL GREATLY

W. 23. CRY LAW JOKE

X. 24. MOMS MR LAY ICY

Y. 25. VERSE BE CUT

TOP 25 GOALSCORERS

A. 1. EYE ON NORWAY

B. 2. BORN YACHT BLOB

C. 3. A SWINDLE

D. 4. RYE LOCK JAW

E. =5. LINED NOVELIST

F. =5. EGG OR BEETS

G. =7. JEEPS CONE

H. =7. SING RAGGY

I. 9. HEM HAG RUSK

J. 10. HULLO SPACES

K. 11.ADVENTUROUSLY IRON

L. 12. OATS SPANNER

M. 13. REV HAD DID

N. 14. INDOOR CANAL RIOTS

O. 15. ARM MY TOY LOT

P. 16. MR CLINIC A BAR

Q. 17. NURSE JELLS KANGAROO

R. 18. ACED ONLY

S. 19. SUNBURNT DALLY

T. =20. GROW ALE LEG

U. =20. ICED AS JOYS

V. 22. BY BARN OR SON

W. 23. I AM OCULAR

X. 24. CHARMS RAD FOR US

Y. 25. MAD BACK HIVED

CAREER PATHS

Can you identify the player from the teams they played for?

1. Huddersfield Town ➜ Manchester City ➜ Torino ➜ **United** ➜ Manchester City

2. **United** ➜ Newcastle United ➜ Birmingham City (loan) ➜ South China

3. Bayern Munich ➜ **United** ➜ Chicago Fire

4. Hogaborgs BK ➜ Helsingborgs IF ➜ Feyenoord ➜ Celtic ➜ Barcelona ➜ Helsingborgs IF ➜ **United** (loan) ➜ Raa IF ➜ Hogaborgs BK

5. Independiente ➜ **United** ➜ Villarreal ➜ Atletico Madrid ➜ Internazionale ➜ Internacional ➜ Cerezo Osaka ➜ Penarol ➜ Mumbai City ➜ Kitchee

6. Aston Villa ➜ Chelsea ➜ Arsenal ➜ **United** ➜ Portsmouth ➜ Crystal Palace ➜ California Surf

7. Shelbourne ➜ **United** ➜ Bolton Wanderers ➜ Detroit Express

8. **United** ➜ Brighton & Hove Albion ➜ Leeds United ➜ Oldham Athletic ➜ Scarborough ➜ Oldham Athletic

9. **United** ➜ Sunderland ➜ Middlesbrough

10. Rennes ➜ Internazionale ➜ **United** ➜ Arsenal ➜ Werder Bremen ➜ Portland Timbers ➜ Chennaiyin

11. Penarol ➜ **United** ➜ Real Madrid B (loan) ➜ Eintracht Frankfurt (loan) ➜ Penarol ➜ FC Copenhagen ➜ Dynamo Moscow (loan ➜ then permanent)

12. **United** ➜ Newcastle United (loan) ➜ Parma (loan) ➜ Villarreal ➜ Fiorentina ➜ Levante (loan) ➜ Celta Vigo (loan) ➜ Genoa ➜ Real Salt Lake ➜ SPAL

13. Middlesbrough ➜ Darlington (loan) ➜ **United** ➜ Middlesbrough

14. Feyenoord ➜ Arsenal ➜ **United** ➜ Fenerbahce ➜ Feyenoord

15. Bayern Munich ➜ **United** ➜ Manchester City

16. Fluminense (youth) ➜ **United** ➜ Lyon ➜ Istanbul Basaksehir ➜ Botafogo

17. Nottingham Forest ➜ Arsenal ➜ **United** ➜ Sheffield Wednesday ➜ Barnsley ➜ Middlesbrough

18. AC Milan ➜ Padova (loan) ➜ Palermo ➜ Torino ➜ **United** ➜ Parma ➜ Internazionale (loan ➜ then permanent)

19. Cobh Ramblers ➜ Nottingham Forest ➜ **United** ➜ Celtic

20. Zirka Kirovohrad ➜ Dynamo Kyiv ➜ Shakhtar Donetsk ➜ **United** ➜ Everton ➜ Fiorentina ➜ Rangers ➜ Manchester City (loan) ➜ Southampton ➜ Al Hilal ➜ Dynamo Moscow ➜ Saturn Ramenskoye ➜ Krylia Sovetov

21. Barcelona (youth) ➜ **United** ➜ Real Zaragoza (loan) ➜ Barcelona

22. Vejle Boldklub ➜ **United** ➜ Saint-Etienne ➜ AS Monaco ➜ Pescara ➜ Vejle Boldklub ➜ AGF

23. Maidstone United ➜ Fulham ➜ **United** ➜ Roma (loan ➜ then permanent)

24. Malmo FF ➜ Ajax ➜ Juventus ➜ Internazionale ➜ Barcelona ➜ AC Milan (loan ➜ then permanent) ➜ Paris Saint-Germain ➜ **United** ➜ LA Galaxy ➜ AC Milan

25. **United** ➜ Leicester City (loan) ➜ Watford (loan) ➜ Wigan Athletic (loan) ➜ Aston Villa (loan) ➜ Everton ➜ Watford (loan ➜ then permanent)

26. York City ➜ **United** ➜ Middlesbrough ➜ West Bromwich Albion ➜ Fulham (loan ➜ then permanent) ➜ Nottingham Forest ➜ Barnsley (loan) ➜ Tadcaster Albion ➜ York City ➜ Tadcaster Albion

27. Blackburn Rovers ➜ **United** ➜ Huddersfield Town (loan) ➜ Burnley ➜ Bacup Borough

28. Kyoto Purple Sanga ➜ PSV Eindhoven ➜ **United** ➜ Queens Park Rangers ➜ PSV Eindhoven (loan)

29. Anderlecht ➜ Chelsea ➜ West Bromwich Albion (loan) ➜ Everton (loan ➜ then permanent) ➜ **United** ➜ Internazionale ➜ Chelsea

30. Aston Villa ➜ **United** ➜ Blackburn Rovers ➜ Birmingham City ➜ Sydney FC ➜ Sunderland

31. Metz ➜ Newcastle United (loan) ➜ Fulham ➜ **United** ➜ Everton ➜ Tottenham Hotspur ➜ Sunderland ➜ Lazio

32. Swansea City ➜ Shrewsbury Town (loan) ➜ **United** ➜ Leeds United

33. Strasbourg ➜ Southampton ➜ **United** ➜ Everton ➜ Nice

34. Everton ➜ **United** ➜ Everton ➜ DC United ➜ Derby County

35. West Ham United ➜ Swindon Town (loan) ➜ Birmingham City (loan) ➜ Tottenham Hotspur ➜ **United**

36. Celtic ➜ **United** ➜ Swindon Town

37. **United** ➜ Leeds United ➜ West Bromwich Albion ➜ Philadelphia Fury ➜ Shamrock Rovers

38. Morton ➜ Leeds United ➜ **United** ➜ AC Milan ➜ Verona ➜ Southampton ➜ Bristol City

39. Leeds United ➜ Oldham Athletic ➜ **United** ➜ Wolverhampton Wanderers

40. PSV Eindhoven ➜ **United** ➜ Lyon ➜ Barcelona

41. Burnley ➜ Norwich City ➜ **United** ➜ West Bromwich Albion

42. Leeds United ➜ Birmingham City ➜ Stoke City ➜ **United** ➜ Crewe Alexandra ➜ Toronto Blizzard ➜ Port Vale ➜ Rochdale

43. West Ham United ➜ Bournemouth (loan) ➜ Leeds United ➜ **United** ➜ Queens Park Rangers

44. Standard Liege ➜ Everton ➜ **United** ➜ Shandong Luneng

45. Estudiantes ➜ Spartak Moscow ➜ Sporting Lisbon ➜ **United** ➜ Estudiantes (loan) ➜ Boca Juniors

46. **United** ➜ Royal Antwerp (loan) ➜ Wolverhampton Wanderers (loan) ➜ Everton ➜ Sunderland ➜ Wigan Athletic ➜ Salford City

47. Millwall ➜ Aldershot (loan) ➜ Djurgardens IF (loan) ➜ Nottingham Forest ➜ Tottenham Hotspur ➜ **United** ➜ Tottenham Hotspur ➜ Portsmouth ➜ West Ham United ➜ Colchester United

48. Hull City ➜ Wigan Athletic ➜ **United** ➜ West Ham United ➜ Rangers ➜ Derby County ➜ Odense BK ➜ OFI Crete ➜ Olympiacos ➜ Notts County ➜ Linfield ➜ FC Mindwell ➜ Dungannon Swifts

49. Stockport County ➜ Arsenal ➜ **United** ➜ Stoke City ➜ Waterford

50. Watford ➜ Aston Villa ➜ **United** ➜ Internazionale ➜ Aston Villa

PLAYERS OF THE YEAR

The official Manchester United Player of the Year award – now known as the Sir Matt Busby Player of the Year – was first presented in 1988, but in actual fact there has been some manner of Player of the Year presentation since the 1971/72 season. But can you look back at each season and recall – or guess! – which mens' team player may have named the best in show for that campaign? To give you a clue we've provided the amount of appearances made and goals scored in all competitions by the winning player, but beware – statistics at times can be misleading!

MANCHESTER UNITED SUPPORTERS' CLUB PLAYER OF THE YEAR

Year		App	Gls
1971/72	____________	48	3
1972/73	____________	44	4
1973/74	____________	37	2
1974/75	____________	47	18
1975/76	____________	45	15
1976/77	____________	57	5
1977/78	____________	52	9
1978/79	____________	44	17
1979/80	____________	36	13
1980/81	____________	37	15
1981/82	____________	45	1
1982/83	____________	49	15

Year		App	Gls
1983/84	______________________	56	5
1984/85	______________________	55	24

SHARP/ MANCHESTER UNITED PLAYER OF THE YEAR

Year		App	Gls
1985/86	______________________	49	4
1986/87	______________________	40	2
1987/88	______________________	48	31
1988/89	______________________	43	8
1989/90	______________________	46	3
1990/91	______________________	52	21
1991/92	______________________	58	25
1992/93	______________________	47	6
1993/94	______________________	49	25

SIR MATT BUSBY PLAYER OF THE YEAR

Year		App	Gls
1994/95	______	39	15
1995/96	______	38	19
1996/97	______	49	12
1997/98	______	37	9
1998/99	______	55	5
1999/00	______	45	12
2000/01	______	43	21
2001/02	______	49	36
2002/03	______	52	44
2003/04	______	40	6
2004/05	______	39	1
2005/06	______	48	19
2006/07	______	53	23

Year		App	Gls
2007/08	____________	49	42
2008/09	____________	55	7
2009/10	____________	44	34
2010/11	____________	45	20
2011/12	____________	38	6
2012/13	____________	48	30
2013/14	____________	52	0
2014/15	____________	43	0
2015/16	____________	49	0
2016/17	____________	50	2
2017/18	____________	46	0
2018/19	____________	40	1
2019/20	____________	22	12
2020/21	____________	58	28

ANSWERS

EARLY YEARS

1. 1878
2. Lancashire and Yorkshire Railway
3. Blackburn Rovers
4. North Road
5. 10 (10-1 win)
6. Bank Street (or Bank Lane)
7. John Henry Davies
8. Kit colours changed to red and white
9. (James) Ernest Mangnall
10. Scored a hat-trick on his debut
11. Aston Villa
12. Archibald Leith
13. Liverpool
14. 1910/11
15. Scored six goals in a game

16. Joe Cassidy
17. Charlie Roberts
18. George Wall
19. Billy Meredith
20. Sandy Turnbull
21. Joe Spence
22. Frank Barson

23. Hilditch was player-manager
24. Ice cream
25. 7-0
26. James W Gibson
27. Walter Winterbottom
28. Johnny Carey
29. Jack Rowley
30. Manchester United Junior Athletic Club

1946-1959

1. False, it was Busby's first managerial appointment (he had been a player for City and Liverpool)
2. Maine Road (Old Trafford had been bombed in the war)
3. Jack Rowley
4. Jimmy Delaney
5. Stan Pearson
6. John Aston (Senior)
7. Sandy Turnbull's
8. United were runners-up in all of those seasons
9. United's temporary ground Maine Road was being used by Manchester City for their FA Cup home games
10. Johnny Morris
11. It was the club's first game back at Old Trafford since the war

12. He scored three penalties in one game
13. He was United's youngest first-team player, 16 years 105 days
14. Joe Armstrong
15. Mark Jones
16. Floodlights
17. Busby Babes
18. Johnny Berry
19. Roger Byrne
20. Burnley
21. Arsenal
22. 30
23. He played in goal
24. Wolverhampton Wanderers
25. Stan Pearson
26. Allenby Chilton
27. Charlie Mitten
28. Billy 'Liam' Whelan
29. Dennis Viollet
30. Chelsea
31. Roger Byrne
32. Jack Crompton
33. Eddie Colman
34. Blackpool
35. Tommy Taylor

36. Mark Jones
37. Athletic Bilbao
38. Tottenham Hotspur
39. He was United's first ever substitute. He also became the club's youngest ever player, at the age of 16 years and 19 days
40. Ray Wood
41. Billy 'Liam' Whelan
42. Filbert Street
43. David Herd
44. Shamrock Rovers
45. Harry Gregg
46. Arsenal 4-5 United
47. Jimmy Murphy
48. Sheffield Wednesday
49. Dennis Viollet
50. Burnley

THE 1960s

1. Maurice Setters
2. 32
3. Tony Dunne
4. Nobby Stiles
5. Bob Bishop

6. Arsenal
7. David Gaskell
8. Stoke City
9. Britain's worst winter in years caused a 'Big Freeze' which shut down English football
10. Paddy Crerand
11. Dennis Walker
12. Leeds United
13. Nobby Stiles
14. Everton
15. 17
16. It was the first time the United Trinity of Best, Law and Charlton played together
17. Phil Chisnall
18. Three – David Sadler, John Aston Jr and Jimmy Rimmer (substitute goalkeeper in 1968)
19. Swindon Town
20. Shay Brennan, Tony Dunne and Bill Foulkes
21. United won the league on goal average, having finished level on points with Leeds
22. Louis Edwards
23. The North Stand
24. John Connelly
25. Chelsea

26. Tommy Docherty
27. Jimmy Ryan
28. Harry Gregg
29. David Herd
30. Bobby Noble
31. West Ham United
32. Nottingham Forest
33. David Herd
34. Liverpool
35. Noel Cantwell
36. It was scored by their goalkeeper Pat Jennings
37. Brian Kidd
38. Manchester City
39. George Best
40. George Best, Bobby Charlton, Brian Kidd, Denis Law, John Aston Jr
41. Willie Morgan
42. Estudiantes
43. Juan Sebastian Veron
44. Wilf McGuinness
45. General Manager
46. Bill Foulkes
47. 1964/65
48. Three times

49. Denis Law, five times
50. Four – two Division One titles, European Cup and FA Cup

THE 1970s

1. Watford
2. Bobby Charlton, John Fitzpatrick and Alan Gowling
3. Wilf McGuinness
4. Paddy Crerand
5. Frank O'Farrell
6. Jimmy Nicholl
7. Manchester City
8. United defeated Arsenal 3-1 at Anfield, and West Bromwich Albion 3-1 at The Victoria Ground
9. Luton Town
10. George Graham
11. Lou Macari
12. Bobby Charlton
13. George and Martin Buchan
14. Ian Storey-Moore
15. Stewart Houston
16. Plymouth Argyle
17. Denis Law
18. Alex Stepney

19. Sammy McIlroy
20. Jimmy Rimmer - he won his other medals with Aston Villa
21. Arnie Sidebottom
22. Aston Villa
23. Michael 'Mick' Martin
24. Third – which was also their final league position that season
25. Southampton
26. Jim McCalliog
27. Paddy Roche
28. Tommy Jackson, David McCreery, Sammy McIlroy, Jimmy Nicholl
29. Stuart Pearson
30. Martin Buchan
31. Jim Holton
32. Newcastle United
33. Jimmy Greenhoff
34. Gordon Hill and Stuart Pearson
35. Dave Sexton
36. FC Porto
37. Gary Bailey
38. Joe Jordan – Leeds United
39. Kevin Moran
40. Gordon McQueen
41. Gordon Hill

42. Rangers

43. Mickey Thomas

44. Arsenal

45. Ray Wilkins – Chelsea

46. David McCreery

47. Stuart Pearson

48. Joe Jordan

49. Runners-up – to Liverpool

50. Tottenham Hotspur

THE 1980s

1. Nikola Jovanovic

2. Gary Bailey

3. Mark Hughes

4. Eighth

5. Lou Macari

6. Widzew Lodz

7. Nottingham Forest

8. Arthur Albiston

9. Leicester City – Nikola Jovanovic (2), Steve Coppell, Ashley Grimes and Lou Macari

10. Sammy McIlroy

11. Crewe Alexandra
12. Ron Atkinson – West Bromwich Albion
13. Third
14. Frank Stapleton – Arsenal
15. Watford, Graham Taylor and Elton John
16. Scott McGarvey
17. Ipswich Town – Bobby Robson
18. Remi Moses and Bryan Robson
19. Garry Birtles
20. John Gidman joined United; Mickey Thomas moved to Everton
21. Paul McGrath
22. Mark Hughes and Norman Whiteside
23. Arnold Muhren – Ipswich Town
24. Frank Stapleton
25. Liverpool – Norman Whiteside
26. Steve Coppell
27. Peter Beardsley – Liverpool
28. AFC Bournemouth – Harry Redknapp
29. Bryan Robson
30. Martin Buchan
31. Garth Crooks
32. Colchester United
33. Jesper Olsen – Ajax, and Gordon Strachan – Aberdeen

34. Mike Duxbury
35. AC Milan
36. Mark Hughes
37. Paul McGrath, Kevin Moran and Frank Stapleton
38. Alan Brazil
39. Luton Town
40. Peter Davenport
41. Southampton
42. Brian McClair – Celtic
43. Arsenal
44. Steve Bruce – Norwich City
45. Jim Leighton
46. Darren Ferguson (Alex Ferguson's son)
47. 11th
48. Danny Wallace
49. Mark Hughes and Brian McClair
50. Six – three FA Cup final matches (including replay), two Charity Shields and one League Cup final

EARLY '90s

1. Mark Robins
2. Mark Hughes

3. Jim Leighton
4. Bryan Robson and Neil Webb
5. Netherlands
6. Liverpool
7. Hungary
8. Arsenal
9. Norwich City
10. Andrei Kanchelskis
11. Southampton (1976), Liverpool (1977) and Arsenal (1979)
12. Sixth
13. Steve Bruce
14. Owl – Sheffield Wednesday, nicknamed 'The Owls'
15. Paul Parker
16. Aberdeen
17. Peter Schmeichel
18. Runners-up
19. Ryan Giggs
20. Nottingham Forest (European Cup winners in 1978 and 1979)
21. Crystal Palace
22. Ryan Giggs, Gary Neville, David Beckham and Nicky Butt
23. Eric Harrison
24. Robbie Savage
25. Tottenham Hotspur – Gary Lineker

THE PREMIER LEAGUE ERA

1992/93

1. Sheffield United's Brian Deane
2. Steve Bruce
3. Everton
4. Dion Dublin
5. Mark Hughes
6. The Stretford End terracing had been demolished at the end of the previous season, with the stand built through the season
7. Aston Villa and Norwich City
8. Oldham Athletic
9. Blackburn Rovers
10. Wimbledon
11. Bryan Robson
12. 10 points clear
13. 26 years
14. Nicky Butt, against Oldham Athletic
15. Peter Schmeichel, Steve Bruce, Gary Pallister and Brian McClair

1993/94

1. Roy Keane
2. Arsenal
3. Norwich City away

4. Niall Quinn
5. 3-2 to United
6. 3-3
7. Four
8. Gary Walsh
9. Brian McClair, Darren Ferguson and Colin McKee
10. Swindon Town
11. Blackburn Rovers
12. Steve Bruce and Denis Irwin
13. Eric Cantona
14. Liverpool, in 1985/86
15. Middlesbrough

1994/95

1. Mark Hughes
2. Paul Scholes
3. 4-2
4. Alex Dawson
5. Kevin Pilkington
6. Nicky Butt
7. Keith Gillespie
8. Henning Berg
9. Crystal Palace
10. Five
11. David May

12. Simon Charlton
13. Four, two of these against Nottingham Forest in December
14. Ludek Miklosko
15. Andrei Kanchelskis

1995/96

1. David Beckham
2. Alan Hansen
3. Nicky Butt
4. Southampton
5. Roy Keane
6. William Prunier
7. 6-0
8. Phil Neville
9. Six
10. 17
11. Southampton
12. Defender Lucas Radebe replaced Mark Beeney in goal for Leeds
13. Stuart Pearce
14. Blue and white
15. Four

1996/97

1. David Beckham scored it from the halfway line

2. Jordi Cruyff
3. Sunderland
4. Raimond van der Gouw
5. David Beckham and Eric Cantona
6. Elland Road (Leeds United) and the City Ground (Nottingham Forest)
7. Coventry City
8. 0-0
9. 11 (0-5, 3-6)
10. Middlesbrough
11. Derby County (Baseball Ground)
12. Gary Pallister
13. Eric Cantona
14. Ole Gunnar Solskjaer
15. Eric Cantona

1997/98

1. Five
2. Mark Hughes
3. 13 (7-0, 6-1)
4. Andy Cole
5. Ronnie Wallwork
6. True – Andy Cole (2), David Beckham and Robbie Fowler
7. Newcastle United
8. Six

9. Dion Dublin
10. Four – Henning Berg, Ronny Johnsen, Erik Nevland, Ole Gunnar Solskjaer
11. Selhurst Park (Crystal Palace and Wimbledon)
12. True – 77 points in 1997/98, 75 points in 1996/97
13. David Beckham and Teddy Sheringham
14. Oakwell (Barnsley)
15. Denis Irwin

1998/99

1. Teddy Sheringham
2. West Ham United
3. Two (Everton's Craig Short and Aston Villa's Steve Watson)
4. Peter Schmeichel
5. The Dell
6. Arsenal, Sheffield Wednesday, Middlesbrough
7. Seven (one win, four draws, one defeat)
8. Ronny Johnsen
9. A pre-match power cut at Old Trafford
10. Jordi Cruyff
11. Dwight Yorke
12. Liverpool
13. Brian Kidd
14. Aston Villa
15. Andy Cole

1999/2000

1. Goodison Park
2. Newcastle United
3. Massimo Taibi
4. Mikael Silvestre
5. 0-5
6. Quinton Fortune
7. Arsenal
8. Andy Cole, Ole Gunnar Solskjaer, Dwight Yorke, Paul Scholes
9. 2-2
10. Paulo Wanchope
11. Jaap Stam
12. Four (Mark Bosnich, Nick Culkin, Massimo Taibi, Raimond van der Gouw)
13. Four
14. Chelsea (0-5) and Newcastle (0-3)
15. 11

2000/01

1. Chelsea
2. Fabien Barthez
3. Massimo Taibi
4. Andy Cole, v Newcastle United
5. Bradford City
6. Henning Berg, Blackburn Rovers

7. Arsenal
8. Dwight Yorke
9. Paul Rachubka
10. Andy Goram
11. Ruud van Nistelrooy
12. Bojan Djordjic
13. Arsenal
14. Teddy Sheringham
15. Gary Neville

2001/02

1. He had announced his intention to retire at the end of the 2001/02 season
2. Mike Phelan
3. Steve McClaren
4. Ruud van Nistelrooy
5. Fulham
6. Louis Saha
7. Jaap Stam
8. Laurent Blanc
9. Andy Cole, Laurent Blanc, Ruud van Nistelrooy, Juan Sebastian Veron and David Beckham
10. West Ham
11. Jesper Blomqvist
12. Blackburn Rovers

13. Southampton
14. None
15. Sylvain Wiltord

2002/03

1. Rio Ferdinand
2. Ole Gunnar Solskjaer
3. Loftus Road
4. It was the last derby to be played at Maine Road
5. Jerzy Dudek
6. Phil Neville
7. Middlesbrough
8. Ricardo
9. Ruud van Nistelrooy and Paul Scholes
10. Ryan Giggs
11. Mark Viduka
12. 15
13. David Beckham
14. Paul Scholes
15. Four (1998/99, 1999/00, 2000/01, 2002/03)

2003/04

1. Real Madrid
2. Nicky Butt
3. Ryan Giggs

4. Cameroon
5. Paul Ince and Denis Irwin
6. The Walkers Stadium
7. Darren Fletcher
8. Portsmouth
9. Kleberson
10. They were all headers
11. Southampton
12. Paul Scholes
13. Two
14. Darren Fletcher and Cristiano Ronaldo
15. Arsenal (1st) and Chelsea (2nd)

2004/05

1. Alan Smith
2. Gabriel Heinze
3. Newcastle United
4. Chelsea
5. David Bellion
6. Liverpool
7. Mikael Silvestre
8. Seven
9. United 2 Arsenal 0
10. Battle of the Buffet
11. Wayne Rooney

12. Arsenal 2 United 4
13. John O'Shea
14. Wayne Rooney
15. Third

2005/06

1. True
2. Ben Foster
3. 380
4. Cristiano Ronaldo
5. Liverpool
6. Darren Fletcher
7. Christmas Day
8. Manchester City
9. Rio Ferdinand
10. Giuseppe Rossi and Gerard Pique
11. Eyesight
12. Nine
13. Chelsea
14. 21
15. Wayne Rooney

2006/07

1. Michael Carrick
2. No.16, Roy Keane

3. Sevilla
4. 5-1 v Fulham
5. Paul Scholes
6. Rio Ferdinand
7. Watford
8. John O'Shea
9. Anfield
10. Phil Neville (own goal) and Chris Eagles
11. Cristiano Ronaldo
12. Arsenal
13. Gabriel Heinze
14. Dong Fangzhuo
15. West Ham, Carlos Tevez

2007/08

1. 34
2. 2-0 to United
3. Fraizer Campbell
4. Owen Hargreaves
5. Four
6. Nani
7. Manucho
8. Portsmouth
9. Ben Foster
10. Wes Brown

11. Liverpool
12. Gerard Pique
13. Tevez, with 19 goals – Rooney scored 18
14. Wigan Athletic
15. 17

2008/09

1. Darren Fletcher
2. Dimitar Berbatov
3. 14
4. It was his 100th goal for the club
5. Tomasz Kuszczak
6. Fulham
7. Sunderland
8. Ryan Giggs
9. 5-2 to United
10. Arsenal
11. Gary Neville
12. Darron Gibson
13. Edwin van der Sar, Nemanja Vidic and Cristiano Ronaldo
14. 90
15. Nicolas Anelka

2009/10

1. Birmingham City
2. Michael Owen

3. 96th
4. Nemanja Vidic
5. Chelsea
6. Four
7. They both netted their 100th Premier League goals
8. Emirates Stadium
9. Blackburn Rovers
10. Kissed him
11. Arsenal and Tottenham
12. Dimitar Berbatov
13. 26
14. Patrice Evra
15. Antonio Valencia and Darren Fletcher

2010/11

1. Chris Smalling
2. Score a hat-trick
3. Stoke City
4. October
5. Paul Robinson
6. February
7. Wolves
8. Nani
9. Gary Neville
10. 4-2 to United

11. 36 seconds
12. Blackburn Rovers and Wayne Rooney
13. Blackpool
14. Nemanja Vidic, Javier Hernandez and Nani
15. Edwin van der Sar and Paul Scholes

2011/12

1. John O'Shea
2. Paul Scholes
3. David De Gea
4. Nemanja Vidic
5. Ashley Young
6. Carl Jenkinson
7. October
8. Darren Fletcher
9. Yakubu
10. April
11. Four
12. 1-0 City
13. Sunderland
14. 89
15. Robin van Persie

2012/13

1. Marouane Fellaini
2. No.20

3. Southampton
4. Manchester City
5. Wigan Athletic
6. Michael Carrick
7. Rafael and Nani
8. Romelu Lukaku
9. Javier Hernandez
10. Swansea City
11. Wilfried Zaha
12. 14
13. Anders Lindegaard
14. Wayne Rooney
15. Liverpool

2013/14

1. Wayne Rooney
2. Wembley, for the Community Shield v Wigan
3. Swansea City
4. Juan Mata and Javier Hernandez
5. 64
6. 12
7. Patrice Evra
8. Adnan Januzaj
9. Danny Welbeck
10. Hull City

11. Robin van Persie
12. Nemanja Vidic
13. West Ham United
14. Norwich City
15. James Wilson

2014/15

1. 1989/90
2. Real Madrid
3. Valencia
4. Darren Fletcher
5. Swansea City
6. Danny Welbeck
7. Juventus
8. Di Maria (32; Falcao made 29)
9. Loftus Road
10. Leicester City, Birmingham City, Brighton & Hove Albion, Derby County
11. Ashley Young
12. Juan Mata
13. 4-2
14. Chelsea, Manchester City and Arsenal
15. Steve Bruce

2015/16

1. Kyle Walker

2. Sergio Romero, Memphis Depay, Bastian Schweinsteiger, Morgan Schneiderlin, Matteo Darmian
3. It was the first Premier League fixture played on a Friday since 2004 (excluding Easter and Christmas/New Year games)
4. Ander Herrera
5. Southampton
6. Ruud van Nistelrooy
7. Troy Deeney
8. Four
9. Donald Love
10. 39
11. Crystal Palace
12. It was the last-ever fixture played at the Hammers' Upton Park stadium
13. Two
14. Wayne Rooney
15. Juan Mata

2016/17

1. AFC Bournemouth
2. Marouane Fellaini
3. Mike Phelan
4. Leicester City
5. First
6. Tom Heaton

7. Anthony Martial
8. Sunderland
9. Juan Mata and Zlatan Ibrahimovic
10. 94th minute
11. Middlesbrough
12. 25
13. Josh Harrop, Angel Gomes, Demetri Mitchell and Joel Pereira
14. Manchester City
15. 17

2017/18

1. Victor Lindelof
2. 4-0
3. No.10
4. Antonio Valencia
5. Stoke City
6. Ashley Young
7. Everton
8. True
9. Wembley Stadium
10. Chris Smalling and Romelu Lukaku
11. Alexis Sanchez
12. Watford
13. 37

14. France

15. Brighton & Hove Albion and Huddersfield Town

2018/19

1. Antonio Valencia

2. Daley Blind

3. Diogo Dalot

4. Luke Shaw

5. Fred

6. Liverpool

7. Cardiff City

8. 5-1 to United

9. Marcus Rashford

10. Victor Lindelof

11. 1-0 to United

12. China

13. James Garner

14. Andreas Pereira

15. Paul Pogba

2019/20

1. Ashley Young

2. Chelsea

3. Daniel James

4. Scott McTominay

5. Joshua King
6. Marcus Rashford and Anthony Martial
7. Ashley Young
8. Odion Ighalo
9. Sporting Lisbon
10. Wolverhampton Wanderers
11. Harry Maguire
12. Anthony Martial
13. Tottenham Hotspur
14. Jesse Lingard
15. Leicester City

2020/21

1. Aston Villa
2. Donny van de Beek
3. Wilfried Zaha
4. Alex Telles
5. Bruno Fernandes's winner against Brighton was scored in the 10th minute of injury time, and was awarded after the final whistle had blown, following a VAR review
6. Newcastle United
7. 6-2 to Manchester United
8. Southampton
9. Wan-Bissaka, Rashford, Cavani, Martial (2), McTominay, Fernandes, James

10. Shola Shoretire
11. Luke Shaw
12. Ruud van Nistelrooy and Wayne Rooney
13. Fulham
14. 10,000
15. Rashford with 21 – Cavani scored 17

2021/22

1. Leeds United
2. Bruno Fernandes
3. Raphael Varane
4. Tottenham Hotspur
5. Chelsea
6. Arsenal
7. Fred
8. Brentford and Brighton
9. Norwich City
10. Aston Villa
11. West Ham
12. Anthony Elanga
13. Gary Bailey
14. Harry Maguire
15. Tottenham Hotspur

FA CUP

1. 1880s
2. Marouane Fellaini
3. Walsall
4. George Best
5. Bryan Robson
6. Roy Keane
7. Molineux
8. Middlesbrough
9. Tranmere Rovers
10. Henrik Larsson
11. Ruud van Nistelrooy
12. Aston Villa
13. Watford
14. Manchester City
15. Denis Law
16. Four
17. Brentford
18. Ruud van Nistelrooy
19. Fourth
20. Cristiano Ronaldo
21. Jadon Sancho
22. 8-0

23. Wolverhampton Wanderers

24. Sir Bobby Charlton

25. Nine

26. 1911

27. Manchester City (h), 10 January 1987

28. Chelsea (a), 1 April 2013

29. 2010 – v Leeds, 3 January 2010

30. Eight

31. Newcastle United

32. Reading

33. Accrington Stanley (a)

34. Norman Whiteside

35. Mark Hughes

36. 1990s – five finals (1990, 1994, 1995, 1996 and 1999)

37. Ryan Giggs – four (1994, 1996, 1999 and 2004)

38. Arsenal

39. Southampton (h), 5 February 1992

40. Denis Irwin and Neil Webb (United lost 2-4 on pens)

41. Dennis Bergkamp

42. Romelu Lukaku

43. Villa Park (13 matches)

44. 1900s

45. Seven

46. Rio Ferdinand

47. 23

48. Ruud van Nistelrooy

49. Peter Schmeichel (41 matches)

50. West Ham United

51. Everton and Chelsea

52. Jonny Evans

53. Two – v Millwall (2004) and Arsenal (2005)

54. Bradford City

55. Cardiff City, Swansea City and Wrexham

56. Yeovil Town

57. Liverpool

58. Bristol City

59. West Ham United

60. Tottenham Hotspur

61. Middlesbrough

62. 1989

63. Five – 1979, 1985, 1990 (x2) and 1994

64. 13

65. Danny Welbeck (for Arsenal, 9 March 2015)

66. 21

67. Charity/Community Shield (winners 17 times)

68. Three

69. 1994

70. Three

71. Six
72. 7-1
73. 39
74. Three – 1994, 1995 and 1996
75. 4-1
76. Bill Foulkes
77. Phil Jones
78. Tottenham Hotspur (16 matches)
79. Harry Maguire, v Norwich City (a)
80. Six
81. Two – Maguire and Dalot
82. Nemanja Matic
83. Alexis Sanchez
84. Five
85. Scott McTominay
86. Mark Hughes
87. 26
88. December
89. David Beckham
90. Michael Owen
91. Teddy Sheringham
92. Wayne Rooney
93. Ipswich Town, 10 January 1988
94. 2013 – Chelsea (a)

95. West Bromwich Albion (h), 11 January 1939

96. Alex Stepney (44 appearances)

97. Nine

98. Jose Mourinho

99. Oldham Athletic (1994)

100. Crawley Town

WINNING FA CUP FINALS

THE 1909 FA CUP FINAL

1. Bristol City; Sandy Turnbull

2. Roberts, Meredith, Wall

3. Ernest Mangnall

4. Charlie Roberts

5. Crystal Palace

THE 1948 FA CUP FINAL

1. Blackpool; Rowley, Pearson, Anderson

2. Crompton, Chilton, Pearson

3. Johnny Carey

4. Stanley Matthews

5. Blue

THE 1963 FA CUP FINAL

1. Leicester City; Law, Herd
2. Crerand, Charlton, Law
3. Noel Cantwell
4. Gordon Banks
5. Scottish

THE 1977 FA CUP FINAL

1. Liverpool; Pearson, J Greenhoff
2. Stepney, Macari, Pearson
3. Martin Buchan
4. Jimmy Case
5. Jimmy

THE 1983 FA CUP FINAL REPLAY

1. Brighton and Hove Albion; Robson, Whiteside, Muhren
2. Bailey, Moran, Stapleton
3. Bryan Robson
4. 2-2
5. Thursday

THE 1985 FA CUP FINAL

1. Everton; Whiteside
2. Albiston, Strachan, Hughes
3. Bryan Robson
4. Peter Reid
5. Peter Willis

THE 1990 FA CUP FINAL REPLAY

1. Crystal Palace, Martin
2. Phelan, Webb, McClair
3. Bryan Robson
4. Jim Leighton
5. Steve Coppell

THE 1994 FA CUP FINAL

1. Chelsea; Cantona (2), Hughes, McClair
2. Schmeichel, Parker, Kanchelskis
3. Steve Bruce
4. Brian McClair
5. Glenn Hoddle

THE 1996 FA CUP FINAL

1. Liverpool; Cantona
2. May, Butt, Cole
3. Eric Cantona
4. Paul Scholes and Gary Neville
5. Green and white

THE 1999 FA CUP FINAL

1. Newcastle United; Sheringham, Scholes
2. Johnsen, Beckham, Solskjaer
3. Roy Keane
4. Roy Keane
5. Teddy Sheringham

THE 2004 FA CUP FINAL

1. Millwall; Ronaldo, van Nistelrooy (2)
2. Howard, Brown, Fletcher
3. Roy Keane
4. Roy Carroll
5. Dennis Wise

THE 2016 FA CUP FINAL

1. Crystal Palace; Mata, Lingard
2. Blind, Carrick, Fellaini
3. Wayne Rooney
4. Chris Smalling
5. Wilfried Zaha

EUROPEAN CUP/CHAMPIONS LEAGUE

1. Belgium
2. 12-0 against Anderlecht
3. Real Madrid
4. Red Star Belgrade
5. Ernie Taylor
6. Finland, against HJK Helsinki
7. 5-1
8. Poland
9. George Best

10. Waterford of Ireland

11. AC Milan

12. Roy Keane

13. Ali Sami Yen

14. Galatasaray, IFK Gothenburg, Barcelona

15. Jesper Blomqvist

16. Marcello Lippi

17. Fenerbahce

18. They became the first European team to win at Old Trafford

19. Rapid Vienna

20. David May

21. 0-1 to Dortmund

22. 15

23. Manchester City

24. Andy Cole

25. Fabien Barthez

26. 20

27. Dwight Yorke

28. Antonio Conte

29. Andy Cole and Dwight Yorke

30. Ossie Ardiles

31. Arnold Schwarzenegger

32. Fiorentina, Valencia, Bordeaux

33. Denis Law

34. Bayern Munich

35. The September 11th terror attacks in the United States

36. 8-7 to United

37. Glasgow

38. Zalaegerszeg

39. Diego Forlan

40. Ruud van Nistelrooy

41. Five

42. Tuncay Sanli

43. Gary Neville

44. Jaap Stam

45. 0-0

46. Benfica

47. Henrik Larsson

48. Luciano Spalletti

49. Cristiano Ronaldo against Sporting Lisbon

50. 16

51. Karim Benzema for Lyon

52. Dimitar Berbatov

53. Two (3-0 v Aalborg and Celtic)

54. Jose Mourinho

55. John O'Shea

56. Michael Carrick and Darren Fletcher

57. 7-2

58. Darron Gibson

59. Gabriel Heinze

60. Ralf Rangnick

61. It was the first time a United player had scored two penalties in the same game in the competition

62. One (1-2 to Basel on matchday six)

63. Two

64. Sergio Ramos (own-goal)

65. True (5-0 v Bayer Leverkusen)

66. Robin van Persie

67. Club Brugge

68. As winners of the 2016/17 Europa League

69. Marcus Rashford

70. Sevilla

71. Juan Mata

72. It was the first time a team had overcome a two-away-goal deficit in competition history

73. Marcus Rashford

74. It was United's 100th home win in the competition

75. Jadon Sancho

WINNING EUROPEAN CUP/ CHAMPIONS LEAGUE FINALS

THE 1968 EUROPEAN CUP FINAL

1. Benfica; Charlton, Best, Kidd
2. Stepney, Foulkes, Crerand
3. Bobby Charlton
4. Wembley Stadium
5. Brian Kidd

THE 1999 CHAMPIONS LEAGUE FINAL

1. Bayern Munich; Sheringham, Solskjaer
2. Johnsen, Blomqvist, Cole
3. Peter Schmeichel
4. Blomqvist and Cole
5. Mario Basler

THE 2008 CHAMPIONS LEAGUE FINAL

1. Chelsea; Ronaldo
2. Brown, Hargreaves, Tevez
3. Rio Ferdinand and Ryan Giggs
4. Frank Lampard
5. Tevez, Carrick, Hargreaves, Nani, Anderson, Giggs

OTHER EUROPEAN COMPETITIONS

1. 1963/64, in the European Cup Winners' Cup
2. Tottenham Hotspur
3. Everton, Dundee United, Wrexham and Liverpool
4. The Inter-Cities Fairs Cup
5. By finishing second in the 1963/64 First Division
6. Borussia Dortmund
7. June
8. Ajax
9. Juventus
10. Plymouth's Home Park
11. Valencia
12. Frank Stapleton
13. 2-0 to Barcelona
14. Juventus
15. Paulo Rossi
16. Legia Warsaw
17. Steve Bruce and Brian McClair
18. Atletico Madrid
19. Five – 1963/64, 1977/78, 1983/84, 1990/91 and 1991/92
20. 17 years – 1995 to 2012
21. Ajax
22. Ander Herrera

23. Marcelo Bielsa
24. FC Midtjylland
25. Robin van Persie
26. Celta Vigo
27. Juventus, Ajax, Bayern Munich and Chelsea
28. Kazakhstan
29. Odion Ighalo
30. Cologne
31. Amad Diallo
32. 8-5 to United (6-2 at Old Trafford, 2-3 in Rome)
33. Henrik Mkhitaryan and Chris Smalling
34. Edinson Cavani
35. Henrik Larsson (UEFA Cup) and Radamel Falcao (Europa League)

OTHER EUROPEAN COMPETITIONS – WINNING FINALS

THE 1991 EUROPEAN CUP WINNERS' CUP FINAL

1. Barcelona; Hughes
2. Sealey, Blackmore, Sharpe
3. Bryan Robson and Steve Bruce
4. Feyenoord Stadium, Rotterdam
5. Ronald Koeman

THE 1991 SUPER CUP FINAL

1. Red Star Belgrade; McClair
2. Schmeichel, Martin, Webb
3. Steve Bruce
4. Old Trafford
5. November

THE 2017 EUROPA LEAGUE FINAL

1. Ajax; Pogba, Mkhitaryan
2. Romero, Darmian, Mkhitaryan
3. Wayne Rooney
4. Donny van de Beek
5. Friends Arena, Stockholm

LEAGUE CUP

1. Milk Cup, Littlewoods Cup, Rumbelows Cup, Coca-Cola Cup, Worthington Cup, Carling Cup, Capital One Cup
2. Exeter City, Bradford City
3. Alex Dawson
4. True – United didn't enter in seven of the eight tournaments following 1960/61, until all 92 Football League clubs were required to compete from 1969/70

5. Manchester City
6. Paul Scholes (v Port Vale)
7. Brighton's Goldstone Ground
8. Two (losing finalists in 1983 and 1991)
9. Middlesbrough
10. Brian McClair
11. Bryan Robson
12. Seven
13. Northampton Town, Manchester City, West Ham United, Hull City
14. Gordon Hill
15. Aston Villa (1977) and Nottingham Forest (1978)
16. Bury
17. Diego Forlan
18. 5-4 to Chelsea
19. Juan Mata
20. Blackburn Rovers
21. David Bellion
22. Colchester United
23. Leeds United's Elland Road
24. Marcus Rashford against Chelsea
25. Nemanja Matic

WINNING LEAGUE CUP FINALS

THE 1992 LEAGUE CUP FINAL

1. Nottingham Forest; Brian McClair
2. Parker, Ince, Hughes
3. Roy Keane and Teddy Sheringham
4. Blue
5. Lee Sharpe

THE 2006 LEAGUE CUP FINAL

1. Wigan Athletic; Rooney, Saha, Ronaldo
2. Van der Sar, Brown, Park
3. Cardiff (Millennium Stadium)
4. Gary Neville
5. Alan Smith

THE 2009 LEAGUE CUP FINAL

1. Tottenham Hotspur; 0-0
2. Foster, Nani, Welbeck
3. Giggs, Tevez, Ronaldo, Anderson
4. False – it was the second (after Liverpool v Birmingham in 2001)
5. Rio Ferdinand

THE 2010 LEAGUE CUP FINAL

1. Aston Villa; Michael Owen, Wayne Rooney
2. Kuszczak, Fletcher, Berbatov

3. Ashley Young
4. Nemanja Vidic
5. True

THE 2017 LEAGUE CUP FINAL

1. Southampton; Ibrahimovic, Lingard
2. De Gea, Valencia, Martial
3. False (also met in the 1976 FA Cup final)
4. United (Southampton wore white shirts)
5. Ander Herrera

SIR MATT BUSBY

1. 1909
2. Celtic
3. Manchester City
4. Wales
5. The FA Cup
6. Liverpool
7. Bob Paisley
8. Louis Rocca
9. James W Gibson
10. Jimmy Murphy

11. Manager of Great Britain's football team at the 1948 Olympics
12. Colombia's
13. Bobby Charlton
14. Real Madrid
15. Denis Law
16. 13 – five league titles, one European Cup, two FA Cups and five Charity Shields
17. Director
18. President
19. Jean
20. 1994
21. Everton
22. United won the Treble that day by beating Bayern Munich in the Champions League final in the Nou Camp
23. 1993
24. Heaven
25. Bobby Charlton, George Best and Denis Law

SIR ALEX FERGUSON

1. Govan
2. Chapman

3. Queen's Park
4. Rangers
5. Ayr United
6. East Stirling
7. St Mirren, based in Paisley
8. Aberdeen
9. Jock Stein
10. World Cup 1986, Mexico
11. Manor Ground (Oxford United)
12. Archie Knox
13. John Sivebaek
14. Gary Walsh
15. Runners-up, to Liverpool
16. Ryan Giggs
17. Roy Keane
18. Steve McClaren
19. Six
20. 2010
21. 11 times
22. 1999
23. Harvard
24. 2011
25. *Never Give In*

THE PLAYERS

WILLIAM 'BILLY' MEREDITH

1. Manchester City
2. Ernest Mangnall
3. Wales
4. Winger (or outside-forward)
5. Two (1907/08 and 1910/11)
6. The FA Cup (1909) and Charity Shield (1908 and 1911)
7. The Welsh Wizard
8. True: He played, aged 46 years and 281 days, v Derby County
9. The Professional Footballers' Association (or Players' Union)
10. 335 (scoring 36 goals)

JOHN 'JACK' ROWLEY

1. Bournemouth
2. Two (1937/38 and 1938/39)
3. True (he also scored seven for Spurs v Luton)
4. 'Gunner'
5. Two (in a 4-2 win)
6. Twice (in 1948/49 and 1951/52)
7. Three
8. England
9. 211
10. Ajax

JOHNNY CAREY

1. 1936
2. Three: First Division (1952), FA Cup (1948), Charity Shield (1952)
3. Football Writers' Association Player of the year
4. Promotion to the First Division (in 2nd place)
5. Seven – 1946 to 1953
6. Goalkeeper, after Jack Crompton was taken ill
7. True
8. Old Trafford – 109 games to Maine Road's 67
9. 344 (scoring 17 goals)
10. Blackburn Rovers

DUNCAN EDWARDS

1. Dudley
2. Cardiff City
3. 1953, 1954 and 1955
4. Scotland
5. West Germany
6. Blackpool (in a 4-1 win)
7. Four – two league titles (1955/56 and 1956/57) and two Charity Shields (1956 and 1957)
8. Arsenal (a), on 1 February 1958
9. Sir Bobby Charlton
10. He was 21

TOMMY TAYLOR

1. Barnsley
2. £29,999 (the tea lady getting the other £1 as a tip)
3. 21
4. After – on 17 May 1953, v Argentina
5. Preston North End
6. Three
7. Blackpool
8. True
9. Aston Villa (in our 1957 FA Cup final defeat)
10. 191 apps/131 goals

BILL FOULKES

1. He was a miner
2. A defender
3. Liverpool
4. England (v Northern Ireland)
5. Sheffield Wednesday (h), 19 February 1958
6. Harry Gregg
7. West Ham United (a)
8. The FA Cup (won in 1963)
9. He scored the equaliser in a 3-3 draw, for a 4-3 aggregate win
10. 688 apps/9 goals

BOBBY CHARLTON

1. Charlton Athletic
2. Three – 1954, 1955 and 1956
3. 1958/59 – he scored 29 goals
4. West Germany, at the Mexico World Cup in 1970
5. Two
6. 1966
7. Preston North End
8. Chelsea (a)
9. 2nd position – 758 appearances, behind Ryan Giggs on 963
10. 249

DENIS LAW

1. Aberdeen
2. Torino
3. Huddersfield Town and Manchester City
4. 1964
5. Aston Villa, Ipswich Town, Stoke City and Waterford
6. Two – The United Trinity and another in the Stretford End
7. The King, or The Lawman
8. 404 apps/237 goals
9. 46 – scored in 1963/64
10. Kenny Dalglish

GEORGE BEST

1. Belfast, Northern Ireland
2. West Bromwich Albion
3. First Division title (1964/65)
4. One – he played 59 out of 60 matches
5. Two
6. 1968
7. Queens Park Rangers (a)
8. 470
9. Fulham
10. Charity Shield (1965 and 1967)

MARTIN BUCHAN

1. Frank O'Farrell
2. True – he made four appearances
3. He was the first player to captain cup wins both north and south of the border
4. The Second Division title
5. *Blues*
6. Bolton Wanderers, Derby County, Everton, Manchester City
7. Frank O'Farrell, Tommy Docherty, Dave Sexton, Ron Atkinson
8. Four times – FA Cup in 1976, 1977, 1979; Charity Shield 1977
9. 456
10. Oldham Athletic

STEVE COPPELL

1. Tranmere Rovers
2. Dave Sexton (200 apps)
3. Right winger
4. No.7
5. True – it remains a club record
6. More – Coppell won 42 caps, Hill eight caps
7. One – the 1977 FA Cup final v Liverpool
8. Real Sociedad
9. 70
10. Crystal Palace

BRYAN ROBSON

1. United manager Ron Atkinson
2. Tottenham Hotspur (a)
3. 18 (all competitions)
4. European Cup Winners' Cup
5. 90
6. 99
7. Five times
8. Five
9. Oldham Athletic (in an FA Cup semi-final replay)
10. Middlesbrough

NORMAN WHITESIDE

1. Belfast, Northern Ireland
2. The Shankhill Skinhead
3. Stoke City (h), on 15 May 1982
4. Pele
5. West Ham United (h), 9 March 1985
6. Arsenal (in a 2-1 win)
7. UEFA Cup and European Cup Winners' Cup
8. Anfield
9. Sir Alex Ferguson
10. Everton

MARK HUGHES

1. Port Vale (his first start was v Oxford)
2. Racecourse Ground, Wrexham
3. Burnley, Aston Villa, Millwall, Southampton
4. Bayern Munich (on loan)
5. Super Cup (1991)
6. 1984/85 – 24 goals
7. Six times (in 13 matches)
8. It was United's first goal of the Premier League era
9. Four – he scored in the 1990 FA Cup final (first game), the 1991 Cup Winners' Cup final, the 1994 League Cup final and the 1994 FA Cup final
10. Everton (in the 1995 FA Cup final)

DENIS IRWIN

1. Oldham Athletic
2. Liverpool – in the Charity Shield, at Wembley
3. Norwich City (The Canaries), on 7 September 1991
4. 1993/94
5. Scored two penalties against both Anderlecht and Liverpool
6. One – the 1994 World Cup in the USA
7. Liverpool (a), 5 May 1999
8. 1993/94 and 1998/99
9. 2001/02
10. The Intercontinental Cup (1999)

PETER SCHMEICHEL

1. False – United also signed Paul Parker from QPR
2. Two – League Cup with United, European Championship with Denmark
3. Boleslaw (Gladsaxe is where he was born)
4. Arsenal and Chelsea (both 19 times)
5. 180
6. Five – 1992/93, 1993/94, 1995/96, 1996/97, 1998/99
7. Rotor Volgograd (h), 26 September 1995
8. UEFA Super Cup (1991)
9. Blackburn Rovers, 12 May 1999
10. Sporting Lisbon

ERIC CANTONA

1. Sheffield Wednesday
2. 12
3. Manchester City (h), 6 December 1992
4. Chelsea (a)
5. 1993/94 and 1995/96
6. 1993 – behind Roberto Baggio [1st] and Dennis Bergkamp [2nd]
7. League Cup
8. Bryan Robson before, David Beckham after
9. York City, on 3 October 1995
10. False – it was against West Ham United

ROY KEANE

1. Hughes scored, not Cantona
2. Kispest Honved (a)
3. No.16
4. 17 – Premier League (x7), FA Cup (x4), Charity Shield (x4), Champions League (x1), Intercontinental Cup (x1)
5. True
6. 2000
7. Steve Bruce preceded him; Gary Neville succeeded him
8. Palmeiras, Brazil
9. 480
10. Celtic

RYAN GIGGS

1. Everton (h)
2. Manchester City (h)
3. UEFA Super Cup (19 November 1991)
4. 1997/98
5. True
6. 34
7. A giant key!
8. The Champions League final v Chelsea, on 21 May 2008
9. Hull City (h)
10. Middlesbrough and Tottenham Hotspur

GARY NEVILLE

1. Eight
2. Basel, Lyon, Charlton, Leicester, Middlesbrough, Everton and Aston Villa
3. Sheffield Wednesday
4. West Bromwich Albion (a)
5. League Cup, 2006
6. True – Schmeichel (56 apps), Beckham and Keane (both 55 apps)
7. FA Cups (x3) – he won two League Cups
8. Two – France '98 and Portugal '06
9. Juventus
10. 602

DAVID BECKHAM

1. False – his debut was v Brighton(a), 23 September 1992
2. 1996/97
3. Aston Villa (a), 19 August 1995
4. No.28, no.24 and no.10
5. 1999 – behind Rivaldo
6. Deportivo La Coruna
7. Chelsea and Tottenham Hotspur
8. Three – FA Cup (1996 and 1999), League Cup (2003)
9. Real Madrid (36 caps), LA Galaxy (14), and AC Milan (5)
10. Paris Saint-Germain

PAUL SCHOLES

1. Port Vale (a)
2. Barnsley
3. 11 – 1995/96, 1996/97, 1998/99, 1999/2000, 2000/01, 2002/03, 2006/07, 2007/08, 2008/09, 2010/11, 2012/13
4. Three – 1995/96, 1998/99, and 2003/04
5. No.22
6. Victor Valdes
7. Oldham Athletic
8. Chelsea – 38 matches
9. Scotland – a 2-0 win at Hampden Park
10. 718 appearances

OLE GUNNAR SOLSKJAER

1. Molde
2. One – Jordi Cruyff scored the other
3. Tottenham Hotspur
4. 'The Baby-faced Assassin'
5. False – he replaced Andy Cole in the 81st minute
6. Henning Berg, Ronny Johnsen, Josh King, Erik Nevland
7. 126
8. Charity/ Community Shield
9. Espanyol
10. Cardiff City

RUUD VAN NISTELROOY

1. False. United signed Jaap Stam from PSV in July 1998
2. Liverpool (Charity Shield, 12 August 2001)
3. 2002/03 – 44 goals
4. Sparta Prague (h), 3 November 2004
5. Most penalties scored for the club (28); Rooney scored 27
6. No.10
7. FA Cup (2004), League Cup (2006)
8. 150
9. Real Madrid, SV Hamburg, Malaga
10. PSV Eindhoven

RIO FERDINAND

1. True – 1 April 2000
2. Zalaegerszeg (h), 27 August 2002
3. Liverpool
4. Six – 2002/03, 2006/07, 2007/08, 2008/09, 2010/11, 2012/13
5. The FA Cup
6. Two – in 2002 and 2006
7. Anton
8. Swansea City, 12 May 2013
9. No.6
10. Queens Park Rangers

NEMANJA VIDIC

1. Spartak Moscow
2. Evra – v Man City (a), 14 January 2006
3. 'Vida'
4. Didier Drogba
5. Zenit Saint Petersburg
6. Gamba Osaka (a 5-3 win)
7. LDU Quito
8. 2011-14
9. 300
10. Internazionale

CRISTIANO RONALDO

1. Sporting Lisbon
2. Bolton Wanderers
3. Portsmouth (h), 1 November 2003
4. Wes Brown
5. 2008
6. 2008/09 – the winner was Nemanja Vidic
7. United (x3) – Real Madrid (x2), Juventus (x2)
8. Nani
9. Six (in seven games)
10. Norwich City

WAYNE ROONEY

1. Fenerbahce
2. Portsmouth and West Ham United
3. Three – 2004/05, 2005/06 and 2006/07
4. False – he scored twice for United at Goodison
5. 2009/10
6. Four – FA Cup (2016), Community Shield (2016), League Cup 2017, Europa League (2017)
7. DC United – v USA, 15 November 2018
8. 253
9. Louis van Gaal (78 games) – he played 39 under Mourinho
10. Derby County

DAVID DE GEA

1. Madrid
2. Manchester City – United won 3-2
3. West Bromwich Albion (a)
4. 2017/18
5. 2014
6. One – in 2012/13
7. Romelu Lukaku
8. Granada and Villarreal
9. False – only Stepney has (539 apps), Schmeichel (398 apps)
10. Three – FA Cup (2016), League Cup (2017), Europa League (2021)

BRUNO FERNANDES

1. Sporting Lisbon
2. Wolverhampton Wanderers
3. Everton (a) – after penalties v Watford (h) and Club Brugge (h)
4. Anthony Martial
5. Brighton & Hove Albion (a) – United won 3-2
6. No.18
7. Everton (h), 6 February 2021
8. Luke Shaw
9. UEFA Nations League
10. Leeds United

MANCHESTER UNITED WOMEN

1. Prenton Park (Tranmere Rovers)
2. Siobhan Chamberlain, Alex Greenwood and Amy Turner
3. Six – Lauren James, Jess Sigsworth, Katie Zelem, Kirsty Hanson, Mollie Green and Ella Toone
4. Durham
5. Tottenham Hotspur and Leicester City
6. 9-0 to United
7. Brighton & Hove Albion
8. Semi-finals
9. Millie Turner
10. Jess Sigsworth
11. Lauren James
12. Jane Ross
13. Birmingham City, Everton and Leicester City
14. Kirsty Hanson
15. Five
16. Reading
17. 1-1
18. Everton
19. Ella Toone
20. 1.64
21. Millie Turner

22. Birmingham City
23. West Ham United
24. Continental League Cup
25. Bristol City
26. Maria Thorisdottir
27. Aston Villa
28. 2-0 to United
29. Burnley
30. Leicester City
31. Kirsty Hanson
32. 2-0 to United (v Reading)
33. Ella Toone and Alessia Russo
34. December 2021 and January 2022
35. Ella Toone and Leah Galton
36. Lyon
37. Karna Solskjaer
38. Katie Zelem
39. 20,241
40. Mary Earps *Correct up to 29/04/2022
41. Katie Zelem, Hayley Ladd and Ona Batlle
42. Everton and Manchester City
43. Norway
44. Martha Harris
45. Katie Zelem

46. Alex Greenwood and Jackie Groenen

47. Quarter-finals (2018/19)

48. Leicester City

49. Ewen Fields (Hyde FC)

50. Mollie Green

HAT-TRICKS

1. Denis Law, with 18

2. Charlie Sagar, against Bristol City in 1905

3. Harold Halse in the 1911 Charity Shield against Swindon Town, and George Best against Northampton Town in the 1970 FA Cup

4. Wayne Rooney, with eight. Ruud van Nistelrooy scored six

5. Denmark's Jesper Olsen, against West Brom in 1986

6. Newcastle United in 2007/08

7. Shinji Kagawa

8. Southampton, Aston Villa and Olympiacos

9. Teddy Sheringham – United, Portsmouth and Spurs

10. Andrei Kanchelskis, in the 5-0 win over Manchester City

11. Anthony Martial v Sheffield United and Marcus Rashford v RB Leipzig

12. Tommy Taylor and Dennis Viollet

13. Andy Ritchie

14. Saint Etienne

15. Newcastle (Ruud van Nistelrooy home, Paul Scholes away)

16. Jack Rowley

17. Wayne Rooney and Dwight Yorke

18. Wolfsburg

19. Dimitar Berbatov v Blackburn, and Andy Cole v Ipswich

20. Stan Pearson

ANAGRAMS

TOP 25 APPEARANCE-MAKERS

A. 1. Ryan Giggs

B. 2. Bobby Charlton

C. 3. Paul Scholes

D. 4. Bill Foulkes

E. 5. Gary Neville

F. 6. Wayne Rooney

G. 7. Alex Stepney

H. 8. Tony Dunne

I. 9. Denis Irwin

J. 10. Joe Spence

K. 11. Arthur Albiston

L. 12. David De Gea

M. 13. Roy Keane

N. 14. Brian McClair

O. 15. George Best

P. 16. Mark Hughes

Q. 17. Michael Carrick

R. 18. Bryan Robson

S. 19. Martin Buchan

T. 20. Rio Ferdinand

U. 21. Jack Silcock

V. 22. Gary Pallister

W. 23. Jack Rowley

X. 24. Sammy McIlroy

Y. 25. Steve Bruce

TOP 25 GOALSCORERS

A. 1. Wayne Rooney

B. 2. Bobby Charlton

C. 3. Denis Law

D. 4. Jack Rowley

E. =5. Dennis Viollet

F. =5. George Best

G. =7. Joe Spence

H. =7. Ryan Giggs

I. 9. Mark Hughes

J. 10. Paul Scholes

K. 11. Ruud van Nistelrooy

L. 12. Stan Pearson

M. 13. David Herd

N. 14. Cristiano Ronaldo

O. 15. Tommy Taylor

P. 16. Brian McClair

Q. 17. Ole Gunnar Solskjaer

R. 18. Andy Cole

S. 19. Sandy Turnbull

T. =20. George Wall

U. =20. Joe Cassidy

V. 22. Bryan Robson

W. 23. Lou Macari

X. 24. Marcus Rashford

Y. 25. David Beckham

CAREER PATHS

1. Denis Law

2. Nicky Butt

3. Bastian Schweinsteiger

4. Henrik Larsson

5. Diego Forlan

6. George Graham

7. Tony Dunne

8. Andy Ritchie

9. Paddy McNair
10. Mikael Silvestre
11. Guillermo Varela
12. Giuseppe Rossi
13. Gary Pallister
14. Robin van Persie
15. Owen Hargreaves
16. Rafael Da Silva
17. Viv Anderson
18. Matteo Darmian
19. Roy Keane
20. Andrei Kanchelskis
21. Gerard Pique
22. John Sivebaek
23. Chris Smalling
24. Zlatan Ibrahimovic
25. Tom Cleverley
26. Jonathan Greening
27. David May
28. Ji-sung Park
29. Romelu Lukaku
30. Dwight Yorke
31. Louis Saha
32. Daniel James
33. Morgan Schneiderlin

34. Wayne Rooney
35. Michael Carrick
36. Lou Macari
37. Johnny Giles
38. Joe Jordan
39. Denis Irwin
40. Memphis Depay
41. Mike Phelan
42. Jimmy Greenhoff
43. Rio Ferdinand
44. Marouane Fellaini
45. Marcos Rojo
46. Darron Gibson
47. Teddy Sheringham
48. Roy Carroll
49. David Herd
50. Ashley Young

PLAYERS OF THE YEAR

MANCHESTER UNITED SUPPORTERS' CLUB PLAYER OF THE YEAR

1971/72 Willie Morgan
1972/73 Willie Morgan
1973/74 Jim Holton

1974/75	Lou Macari
1975/76	Lou Macari
1976/77	Brian Greenhoff
1977/78	Steve Coppell
1978/79	Jimmy Greenhoff
1979/80	Joe Jordan
1980/81	Joe Jordan
1981/82	Ray Wilkins
1982/83	Bryan Robson
1983/84	Ray Wilkins
1984/85	Mark Hughes

SHARP/ MANCHESTER UNITED PLAYER OF THE YEAR

1985/86	Paul McGrath
1986/87	Paul McGrath
1987/88	Brian McClair
1988/89	Bryan Robson
1989/90	Gary Pallister
1990/91	Mark Hughes
1991/92	Brian McClair
1992/93	Paul Ince
1993/94	Eric Cantona

SIR MATT BUSBY PLAYER OF THE YEAR

1994/95	Andrei Kanchelskis
1995/96	Eric Cantona

1996/97	David Beckham
1997/98	Ryan Giggs
1998/99	Roy Keane
1999/00	Roy Keane
2000/01	Teddy Sheringham
2001/02	Ruud van Nistelrooy
2002/03	Ruud van Nistelrooy
2003/04	Cristiano Ronaldo
2004/05	Gabriel Heinze
2005/06	Wayne Rooney
2006/07	Cristiano Ronaldo
2007/08	Cristiano Ronaldo
2008/09	Nemanja Vidic
2009/10	Wayne Rooney
2010/11	Javier Hernandez
2011/12	Antonio Valencia
2012/13	Robin van Persie
2013/14	David De Gea
2014/15	David De Gea
2015/16	David De Gea
2016/17	Ander Herrera
2017/18	David De Gea
2018/19	Luke Shaw
2019/20	Bruno Fernandes
2020/21	Bruno Fernandes